ANGEL CROSSING

BY
SUSAN KANEY

For information write:
Angel Crossing Publishing
14440 Southbridge Forest Dr.
Charlotte, NC 28273

If you are unable to order this book from your local
bookstore, you may order directly from the
publisher. Quantity discounts for organizations are
available.
See order form in back for ordering information.

10 9 8 7 6 5 4 3 2 1

ISBN 0 – 9678863 – 0 – 9

DEDICATION

This book is dedicated to God.

ACKNOWLEDGEMENTS

I give thanks to God, The Christ Light and to Angel for their Love, and for always being in my life.

Many, many thanks go to Tom Sawyer, a five-star general in the spiritual army; whose guidance, teaching, assistance, love and *grinding* helped make this book possible. In particular, Tom assisted me with the Jesus episode when I found I could not remember all the details of His conversation. With Tom's (and Sidney Farr's) permission, I used exerts from the chapter "I Met You By Love," taken from the book, "Tom Sawyer and The Spiritual Whirlwind," to help fill in the gaps. Knowing that The Christ works very closely with Tom assures me that the information in that chapter is absolutely accurate. I have also known and been influenced by Tom since August of 1987, so additional teachings by him are sprinkled through out the book through the voice of the character Janet.

Who has a heart as big as a mountain? Sidney Farr! Thanks Sidney for your help in editing, for your encouragement and for the big "Wow!" you gave me when you first read ANGEL CROSSING.

Janet Appel should just start her own editing business; she is *SO* good at it. I also want to thank her for allowing me to use her name as Janet/Solomon. Although she is not the Janet/Solomon in my book, she *IS* Janet/Solomon all on her own, and I count it an honor to have her as my friend.

Thanks also to Kelli Thomas and Jeri English, who were sitting with me as I was spitting this information out and whose arms I twisted into reading this material because I just *had* to have somebody's opinion!

With marginal computer abilities, I had to have a lot of help in formatting my book. Cudos to Theundra Livingston for actually doing all of it for me! Thanks Theundra, when you get to heaven you'll get to know exactly how much I appreciate your help.

There were a number of people I contacted and asked to read my manuscript. One of those was Jayne Howard, author of "Commune with the Angels." When I asked her for her thoughts and advice she not only offered her help but volunteered to write a foreword! Jayne, Thank you; I cannot accurately express my appreciation for your encouragement and help.

I would also like to thank Alan Seale author of "On Becoming a 21st - Century Mystic: Pathways to Intuitive Living," for giving me sound, practical advise on publishing.

Anne Atwell, probably my longest known friend, and a spiritual partner in another important area of my life, The Southeastern Conference, also assisted in editing. I deliberately saved her for last in doing my final editing, because I knew she would catch all the little tiny errors and she did. Anne never misses a thing. Thank you Anne, for everything. You know *ALL* the reasons why.

I would like to thank my husband Jerry Baburek for just being his wonderful self. Someday I will have to tell the story of how God introduced the two of us and just let me say that if you ever ask God for a sign, be prepared to get knocked on your keister!

And last, to Jana, my Angel come to earth, thank you for allowing me the opportunity to be your mother. I love you so much, I can hardly say your name without my eyes leaking.

FOREWORD

In my travels as a lecturer about the Angelic Kingdom, people often ask me if there are failsafe techniques that allows one to know that the life choices being made are correct. The only safety net that we have is faith in God. ANGEL CROSSING is a testimony to the power of walking in faith. Susan Kaney is one of God's Faith Walkers.

I feel privileged to have the honor of writing the forward for Susan Kaney's ANGEL CROSSING. First on a personal level as I have the abundant blessing of knowing Susan as a friend. The precious personality of Susan comes through loud and clear in ANGEL CROSSING. She is without a doubt a divinely delightful human being.

Yet more than friendship, I am honored to write the forward as ANGEL CROSSING conveys to readers that more times than not we go kicking and screaming when Spirit calls us to our higher purpose. Susan writes with honesty and openness and shares with readers the questions, doubts, fears and uncertainties that she was processing in the midst of a truly transformational experience. She went from someone hiking the path of a mountain to a wayshower on the path of life. Her book is a trailblazing guidebook as it opens readers to not only visitation and inspiration by God's Angels, but witnessing the Light of Christ.

In my service with Angels, I encourage people to read and re-read the 91st Psalm because of its ability to bring comfort to the soul. I felt that same comforting energy conveyed in reading Susan's accounting of her experience with Christ and the words He spoke to her. I have found myself returning to those words for they truly radiate peace and tranquility.

During Susan's encounter with Christ, she writes, "Jesus kept encouraging me to move..." I feel 𝒜NGEL 𝒞ROSSING is just that – encouragement from Jesus: For the LOVE OF GOD move closer.

Jayne Howard
Author of Commune with the Angels

INTRODUCTION

When I was a young girl of seventeen, I began having out-of-body experiences in a most dramatic way. Completely wide-awake, I was pulled out of my body by a Being made of Light and told that I had been born for a specific reason. My mission was set for the future, but I was to start preparing for it at that young age, without knowing the specific assignment. Out of the ordinary experiences have occurred through out my life, culminating with a face to face meeting with Jesus The Christ on December 25, 1997. At that meeting, I was informed that my preparations were complete and it was time to begin my mission. One of my tasks was to write the following book.

I trust God that He had me write this book exactly the way He wanted. Although in fictional form, the information is true and the spiritual experiences are real. In order to tell the story, I split myself in half. The character Susan is really myself when I began having my experiences at the age of 17, and the character Janet is the person I have become over the past 25 years. I included only the most profound experiences, and in order to condense this 25-year span of spiritual development, the book covers just five days. Since my experience with Jesus The Christ occurred atop a rock in the Blue Ridge Mountains, I chose this very setting for "ANGEL CROSSING."

There are layers upon layers of messages within these pages, but the most important thing to me is that you enjoy reading it. More than anything this book is an invitation to you. I invite you to ponder on the Glory of

God. My sincerest thanks to you for your time in reading
this information.

Susan Kaney

ANGEL CROSSING

CHAPTER ONE

She told me she was an angel. Can you believe that? As is my habit, I have always kept a diary or journal of unusual occurrences in my life. It is something I started when I was just eleven years old and have continued more or less throughout its entirety so far. The experiences I am about to relate occurred while I was on vacation in the mountains of North Carolina. Specifically, while climbing around the top of Grandfather Mountain in Linville, I came upon a woman sitting on the edge of a rock cliff near the swinging bridge, looking across a fifty-mile view of mountains and valleys. She invited me to share the magnificent view, and while sitting with her, she asked me if she could share something with me. When I answered, "Of course," she told me she was an angel.

I stood up quickly. Naturally, I was taken aback. I was obviously talking to a mentally disturbed woman and I'm sure I looked as skeptical as I felt. I studied her for a moment, taking in the fact that she was certainly a human being, looking to be somewhere in her mid-thirties or early forties; about my age, with brown eyes and light brown, wavy hair.

Maybe she had a high stress job and was having a nervous breakdown. I could understand that. I knew all about high level stress. As a matter of fact, too much stress was why I was in the mountains now, even away from my family, trying to get away for a little while from a job that I loved, but was running me ragged from morning to night.

"Uh...excuse me..." I stammered a little, "I don't want to offend you or anything, but you look human to me."

"Yes, I'm human."

"But, you just told me you're an angel."

"Right," she said, then sighed. "I am both." She gave me a sideways glance and then laughed. "I guess you think I'm crazy. I don't blame you. It's certainly not something one hears every day. I didn't tell you this to alarm you; it's just that I've never shared this with anyone before, and I just feel like it would be good if I could share some information with you. That is, if you would be willing to listen to me?"

I waited a moment before answering, because a lot of thoughts were going around in my head. From just an eyeball glance, the woman SEEMED sane enough, but what if she wasn't? Was it a good idea for me to sit and listen to this woman, if she was just someone in need of a lot of therapy? And what if she was physically dangerous? She looked harmless enough, but a person could never tell. She appeared to be in pretty good shape for her age, and I wasn't sure I was up to struggling with someone who might take the sudden urge to throw me over the side of the mountain, especially maybe, if God told her to do it!

On the other hand, what if she were really what she claimed to be and I turned down the opportunity to get information from an angel? I certainly wasn't totally opposed to the possibility, although to call me a "doubting Thomas" would be putting it lightly. Of course, I had come to the mountains to hike, not to sit and take notes. I continued to think about it for a moment, and then decided that if she were willing to hike with me, I could at least listen to what she had to say, and, if I found it interesting, I could then record it into my journal at night at the motel I was staying in. I wasn't worried about forgetting anything by the end of the day, because my habit of journaling was so strong from years of writing that I had developed a keen short-term memory on a day to day basis. Once I recorded my day's events, I then "let go" of the recorded day's memories. Also, I reminded myself, I was an ex-police officer and was still in pretty good shape myself, so if I did end up struggling with her, I would probably be okay. Before I made my final decision, however, I wanted to know her name, so I asked.

"Janet," she responded, "but all my friends call me Solomon."

"Well, you couldn't call me a friend. I mean, we just met today."

"That's what you think," she responded with a grin.

Yeah, right. I cursed myself at that moment for a streak of kindness that I possess, which is, unfortunately, a mile wide and has the effect of leaving me totally incapable of hurting other people's feelings. A part of me just wanted to say, "Lady, you're nuts," so I could just turn and walk away, but I couldn't do it. I stood there in hesitation, then she asked me my name.

"Susan," I told her, then added sarcastically, "But, hey, you can call me Grace."

"Is that what your friends call you?" she asked.

"No, nobody, but I figure if I'm to call you Solomon, why not "Grace" for me?"

Okay, admittedly that was a little mean, but that was as far as I could take it. All she did was laugh, so I made my decision. "I'm going to be in the mountains for a week," I told her. "I am willing to listen to you today, if you are willing to hike with me on the mountain trail. If things go well... we can see." Then I explained to her my habit of daily journaling and asked her if she would mind if I recorded our conversation on paper.

She smiled. "Actually, that would be perfect."

I smiled back. "Well then, shall we start hiking?" We both rose and made our way to the mountain trail that leads to McCrae Peak. The Grandfather Mountain trail is open to all visitors, but it's not an easy hike. There are stairs and rope climbs to negotiate, and it can be dangerous if one is not careful. There are plenty of breath-taking views along the trail, and we would often stop to rest and appreciate the scenery. We started exchanging the usual type of information as we walked along: where we lived, jobs, etc...and then because the information I was hearing just seemed to make her seem more and more human, I asked, "Would you mind telling me how you can be both an angel and a human at the same time?"

"That's a good place to start," she responded. "I originated in Heaven. I was created directly by God to be a messenger, a go-between, for Him and the people of the earth. I did that for centuries, bringing help and assistance, or messages, whenever needed. But, as time passed here on earth, a change started to occur. It became more and more difficult for people to perceive God's energies, or angels. The messages were going unheard. The energies between the two became denser and denser to where it took tremendous energy for a person on the earth to barely perceive any guidance from angels. Direct manifestations have gone completely unseen. It has reached the point where only a small percentage of people on the earth are open and able to feel or experience any guidance at all."

"How sad!" I interjected.

She gave a sad smile. "It is sad, because to be in touch with the Glory that is God is the most joyful experience that can be had. And there are millions who are unable to experience God at all."

As I listened, I noticed that I was starting to feel at ease about her. I figured if she was a person in need of therapy, at least she was a harmless person in need of therapy. She had a very gentle air about her, as if it were her nature to calm and soothe, and I could tell that she was projecting that energy toward me as she spoke.

"I want you to understand that what I am about to tell you is more like an analogy rather than what really was. Away from earth, communication does not take place with words. Communication occurs as a whole, not in pieces. The original created thought, occurring perfectly, is projected in its entirety. There is full, total understanding, occurring instantaneously, without any process necessary at all."

"So, what is it you're trying to tell me?"

"That what I'm about to tell you is true enough for Earth terminology, but it isn't what really occurred, and I am not able to put into words the actual occurrence that took place because there were no words to begin with."

"Okay, I get you; so go ahead and give me the analogy."

"Alright. We could say that God looked down upon the earth and was very unhappy with what he saw. His beautiful, lovely Earth, the jewel of the universe, was being desecrated and it was the fault of mankind. Earth called to God, "Help me, I am being poisoned! I am dying, everything will be destroyed unless something is done!" God had foreseen this event and had, in the past, sent any number of teachers, including His own Son at one time, but to no avail. Even having sent His own Son had not turned mankind around. His Son taught love and peace, but mankind used His name and God's to carry out killing and destruction upon one another. No, things were not going well for Earth and God had a decision to make. He could, in a blink of an eye, remove all of mankind from the face of the Earth, and that would certainly save the planet from further destruction, but, out of His love for them, He decided to give mankind one more chance. And to help mankind, God called for an army of his own. This army was a volunteer army; a spiritual army, with the whole purpose being to show mankind God's love and pointing the way to God."

"A spiritual army..." I breathed. "How many?"

"Thousands," she responded, "Not all are angels; some are highly evolved souls who had been to Earth in the past, but had not been in a long time."

"So, let me get this straight. God decided the earth needed help, so he called upon highly evolved souls and angels for a spiritual army?" She nodded affirmatively and I continued. "Okay, so there are thousands of beings like you on the earth now...how come we haven't heard more declarations being made like you've made to me? I'd think if there were lots of real angels around, the press would have heard about it by now."

"It doesn't exactly work that way."

"That figures. So, how does it work?"

"Let's continue with my analogy. When God made the call through out the universe, thousands responded. Experienced souls, souls who had never visited earth and angels all volunteered to do God's will. The Christ, who had been on earth as Jesus, told us all about his experiences here as a man. He warned us that even when he was here, the vibrations were very dense and harsher than he had expected, and that in the two thousand years that had passed since he was here, the energy vibrations had become much, much worse. He told us that he had actually only accomplished a little of what he had desired to do. The difficulty being how far mankind had actually separated from God, and the amount of energy it took to try to bridge the gap that had taken place. After two thousand years, even with The Christ having been on earth, the energy of mankind as a whole has only become more dense." She stopped and sighed deeply, and I sensed a deep sadness.

"What is it?" I asked gently.

She looked at me and I saw tears swimming in her eyes. "Seventy-five percent," she faltered and then wiped her eyes, "Seventy-five percent of the entire population of the earth is spiritually dysfunctional."

"Say what?!" I exclaimed. "Seventy-five percent of the whole world population?! Jeez Louise! Are you sure about that? Seventy-five percent? That can't be right!"

"Oh, it's right," she said, gaining control of her emotions. "You see, mankind's natural state of being is to BE spiritual. The problem that has occurred is that mankind, through acts of free will and states of denial, has built up walls between themselves and God, consciously and subconsciously. The walls built up by mankind have become SO dense that even in times of great trauma or great need, where spirituality alone is the motivating force for survival as well as progress, they remain dysfunctional."

"I'm not sure I understand," I said, shaking my head. "Can you explain further or give an example?"

"Okay," she nodded, then lifted her eyes, seeming to stare into space, and then I had the impression that she was listening to someone. "Okay," she said again, "Have you ever heard the expression, 'Can God make a rock so big that even He can't lift it?"

"No, can't say that I have."

"It's a paradoxical oxymoron used by some to show that God is fallible."

"Huh?"

She laughed, "You know...can God do anything? Well, if God can do anything, can he make a rock so big that even he can't lift it? Well...the answer is Yes. But then, if God makes a rock so big he can't lift it, then he can't do everything!"

"Oh..." I said slowly, trying hard to understand, but not really. "Does that mean, God can't do everything?"

"No." She answered emphatically. "God can do everything and anything. What people don't understand is the true nature of God in the first place, and in this instance the rock that we've been talking about has been created by Man and not God."

"I haven't got the slightest idea what you're talking about."

"That's good! That will leave you more open."

I was starting to feel a little dizzy with thought, and as we were just reaching the place where the upper ladder climbs were about to begin for McCrae Peak, I asked her if we could hold the talk for a few minutes to concentrate on the climb. On this magnificent trail there are a series of five ladders that have been nailed right into the rock wall of the mountain. Where the top ladder ends is a one inch thick wire "rope" that a person must grab hold of in order to pull himself up the rest of the way to the cliff. It's not difficult to maneuver, but it's a place where you definitely want to be sure footed and strong handed. Although I had done the trail numerous times, this time, like every time I had ever done it, I felt my stomach flip over as I reached for the wire and pulled myself up and over the ridge.

My stomach flipped over. I feel a need to interject here just why that's an important statement to me. There had been a time, and in truth it was only several years ago, when I was incapable of making this climb at all. It seems rather paradoxical to have a strong love for the mountains and yet have a horrible fear of heights doesn't it? Oh, but I did! Being the strong-willed person that I am, however, I decided I needed to conquer that fear and set about doing so by deciding to take this trail on Grandfather Mountain as a cure. Sadly to say, Grandfather defeated me. On these very step ladders, going straight up the face of the cliff, I froze in absolute panic, breaking out in beads of sweat as I clung to the old wooden ladder, unable to either move forward, or climb back down. It was a cool day in the fall and I had seen no other hikers. I had nightmarish visions of being stuck on the mountainside all during the night, until overcome with exhaustion and cold, falling to my death.

Fortunately for me, though I suffered great depths of humiliation and extreme embarrassment, I was saved by another hiker and his ten-year-old son. The other hiker easily recognized my fright and suggested it might be easier for me to continue going up the climb rather than try to go back down. At that time, for my fear level, it was the wrong decision, but I allowed the man to talk me up the ladders and the steel rope pull, one step at a time. I cannot begin to explain the low level of degradation I felt as I was unable to hide the fact that I trembled all over. My hands shook so badly and my palms were so wet from perspiration, that it was difficult for me to grasp either the ladders or the pull. I became intimately acquainted with the rock face of the mountain and its pebbly but smooth, worn, grey surface. Upon reaching the top and the area where the mountain falls away on both sides, I could not even stand up! No, instead, I crawled on my hands and knees, with my nose to the ground, until I could get to the area where I could go back down the mountain on a longer, but safer route. For a full week thereafter, I came to this trail every single day, going as far as I could before I would stop from fear. When caught in the fear, I would sit down wherever I was until the fear passed and I could go a little further. It took me the entire week to complete this one climb to McCrae Peak. Upon completion of the hike, however, I was jubilant with elation at my success. Conquering the climb had indeed removed almost all my fears of heights. Okay, I did say almost. Even now, I am uncomfortable standing at the very edge of a cliff side, or even seeing another person standing at the edge of a deep drop. Compared to what I used to feel, however, I feel I can say I am cured of the deeper fears.

The view from the point just after you pull yourself up and over the ridge is spectacular and is a definite place to then turn and gaze back over the valley. Janet and I sat and gazed at the view of various greens from trees and bushes around and below. After a while of silent viewing, I turned back to this woman, whom I now was becoming convinced knew "something," even if I wasn't sure she was an angel. "Okay, you want to try again?"

"Let me just say that God is always with all of us. The Christ... when he said he would never leave us... didn't. He is here. So what's the problem? Well, mankind is the problem. God gave mankind the gift of free will. Free will is the power to create... anything. It's your choice what you want to experience. In the beginning of mankind's existence, men and women experienced full communication with God, freely and daily. There was no separation spiritually. The Bible speaks of Adam and Eve and the apple and the snake. The story is basically the symbolism of man's first decision that caused the first separation of mankind from God; a block had been created which prevented the complete free-flow of energy between God and his creation. But that wasn't the worst. There was still communication going on. However, over time, mankind continued to make free-will choices that further and further separated him from God...or let us say, that prevented him from "hearing" God, because like I said, God never left mankind, mankind left God. God saw what was happening, and could see where it was leading. So, every now and then God would send a great teacher down to try and awaken people to what they were doing. Some people were helped, but unfortunately, things just got gradually worse and worse, and denser and denser."

"Denser?" I asked, "what do you mean denser?"

"The energy," she answered. "Everything is energy. You could say, in the simplest terms, that God is the highest, purest and most refined energy there is. Every single step removed from God is a slightly denser energy. The further you move away from God, the denser the energy."

"So, here on earth, the energy is the densest?"

"You would not be able to comprehend just how dense. And the worst of it is, the dense energy created by mankind, the wall that is so thick, so huge, so heavy and cannot be seen by the physical eyes, is virtually impenetrable by mankind."

"So this is the rock that God created which is so big, God cannot lift it?"

"It's not a barrier to God. God can move right through it and does. It's only a barrier to mankind, because although God gave the gift, mankind made the creation and mankind cannot see or hear through what he has created. The wonderful energy that is God flows through us and around us all the time. He sings his love to us, his call to us never ceases. Few hear, see or feel him."

"So, now we're back to the fact that seventy-five percent of the world population is uh...spiritually dysfunctional...because they have no connection to God. Is that right?"

"On the head."

I don't know why, but I felt contrary. There was just something about that statement that made me angry and the more I thought about it the angrier I became. I could not help the outburst that came forth.

"Do you have any idea just how many churches and religious organizations there are around the world? In the United States alone, for Pete's sake! The United States is mostly a nation filled with Christian churches, not to mention Judaism, Buddhism and the rest. I mean, come on! You're only leaving twenty-five percent of the whole world population as being in touch with God! That cannot be right!"

I wanted to provoke her. I wanted to see her as agitated as I was. I waited for a reaction, but didn't get one. She was sitting serenely on the rock with her knees up against her chest; arms wrapped around them, staring out into the vista, apparently in a whole other world. I slapped my hands down on the rock in agitation and stood up. I began to pace on the tiny round of rock that jutted out from the mountain peak.

"Seventy-five percent, seventy-five percent!" I mumbled it over and over. I finally stopped and turned to her. "I'm sorry, but I just don't believe that only twenty-five percent of the world population is in tune with God. I just don't believe that."

"I'm not asking you to believe me," she said quietly, "I'm not asking you to believe anything at all I've said today."

I felt the wind being knocked out of me. My anger dissolved, but my frustration remained. I again sat down next to her.

"Then what...."

She interrupted. "You don't have to believe anything I say. When I told you there was something I wanted to share with you, all I asked is if you were willing to listen. That's all I want. For you to listen. What you want to believe is your choice alone. Please DO believe whatever makes you feel comfortable, that's your choice, your free-will in action."

I shook my head at her. "Please explain to me how, with all the churches and religious organizations there are in this world, how there could only be twenty-five percent of the population who are not spiritually dysfunctional?"

"Promise you're not going to shoot the messenger?" She smiled at me, and then I felt my frustration leave as well.

I smiled back at her, feeling relief that I had not made her angry, "I'm sorry for my outburst."

"No need to apologize, no offense was taken." She touched me lightly on the hand when she said it and I swear I could feel an unusual warmth and peace flow through my body from her touch. Then she began to speak and her voice was quiet and smooth. I found myself relaxing, though the words she said were terribly distressing.

"Yes, there are many churches, many religious organizations, but do you necessarily think that just because those churches and organizations exist, that all the people who belong to them live their lives with God in their hearts?"

I didn't know what to say or how to respond, so she continued. "Just because a person calls himself a Christian, a Buddhist, a Jew, a Muslim, or whatever sect or religion...just because a person is a member of or calls himself whatever he claims to be, does not make that person a spiritually-oriented person. You seem to find comfort in the fact that all these religions exist. But tell me, which is the true religion? Which one of all these religions, or sects within these religions really holds the truth and heart of God?"

"Well...umm...I was raised to be a Christian."

"Catholic or Protestant?"

"Umm...Methodist."

"So, you were raised to be a Christian and that means you went to a Methodist church, and were told..."

"That in order to get to heaven we have to be saved by Jesus?"

"You answered that like you think I'm testing you here. Relax, I'm not testing you, I was just asking for information."

I relaxed as best I could, but I was bracing myself for information I was sure I would have trouble digesting. She continued. "So, would it be accurate to say that you grew up believing that in order to get to heaven, a person needed to be a Christian because you were told that was the correct religion?"

I felt my heart sink. I stammered, "I guess...basically...that could be true."

She rushed to assure me. "Well, that's all right. It's good to be Christian!" I felt better. Then she continued. "It's good to be Jewish. It's good to be Muslim! It's good to be Catholic, or Buddhist, or Hindu, or whatever!"

"Now wait a minute!" I burst out, "Not two minutes ago, you were just telling me, that just because a person belongs to any of those religions, that doesn't necessarily make them spiritual, or of God!" She started to speak, but I interrupted. "Whoa, wait a minute. You tell me. You tell me which one of all the religions of the world is God's religion?"

"All of them and none of them."

I gave her a look of pure exasperation. "Are you trying to be difficult?!"

Her laughter rang out and bounced from the mountain peaks back to us. "No, not at all! I'm trying to be as clear as I can be!" Then she did something that for some reason totally unnerved me. She turned her gaze on me and held me with her eyes. They were brown and large.... and very, very piercing. I began to feel very uncomfortable and was quite relieved when she spoke again. "Look, God is not a religion. The Christ is not a religion. Mankind has created all the religions based on his belief or beliefs in God. There is only one God, and all religions have been built on some teacher that God sent. So in that sense, all religions are God's religions. However, none of the religions of the world are God's because God is not a religion. God is God. It doesn't matter what religion you claim, what does matter is that you have God, or Love, in your heart."

I felt awkward, wanting to question her further regarding God, but sensed that she wasn't ready to go further in that direction, so instead I said, "You never finished telling me how you, an angel, came to earth."

"Yeah...yeah, guess I got a little sidetracked." She stood up, stretched, then glanced at her watch. " Want to go just a little further before we have to start back? I know there's one more ladder which will put us at the highest point for McCrae Peak."

"Sounds good to me," I responded and we started out again. This part of the trail is probably the most beautiful to me. It's not named this, but I call it "the ridge path." It's just an area probably only two hundred yards in length, lasting until you get to the last ladder climb, but what is truly physically breath snatching, is that it is only five to six feet wide for the entirety. While transversing those two hundred yards, one can see both sides of the mountain falling away. Though my first experience was terrifying, I now find it beautifully awesome. I love the North Carolina Mountains, though certainly not as tall and as rugged as the Swiss Alps, and certainly any serious mountain climber would look at these mountains with disdain, because of lack of challenge. No, it's the sheer beauty of these very ancient ridges. The lushness of vegetation that grows right to the very tops of peaks is so thick, it appears almost tropical.

When we reached the large round rock that marked the highest elevation, we climbed the ladder and once more partook of delicious scenery. After a few minutes, I turned to my companion and spoke. "Well, what's next? I know you didn't finish talking to me about God, but I still get the feeling that you would rather save that for later. Am I right?"

She smiled and nodded. "I often find myself on a tangent about God. I can't seem to help myself; after all, God is my business, so to speak. But, yes, you're right. I would like to save further discussion regarding God for later. I know I haven't yet finished my analogy about how I came to be here on earth, and," she paused, looking at her watch, "it's starting to get late. I would at least like to finish that before we call it a day and head back down."

"So would I," I agreed.

"Let's see, where was I before I got on a tangent?" She looked at me in question, but I just shook my head. I felt like my brain was fried, and for the first time in my life I was worried about getting something "down" correctly in my journal.

After a moment she began, "Okay. I think I've got it. Literally thousands of angels and souls gathered for this great opportunity to serve God. We were warned that by taking a physical body we would be subject to the same physical limitations as any human, and more than likely..."

"Oh, darn." I interrupted.

"What?' She asked looking startled.

"Well, Monica," I said, flippantly referring to her as the character on the popular television show, *Touched By An Angel*, "I was hoping to see you flap some wings, or mysteriously disappear, or at least show that golden glow before the day ended."

Her grin was wide, "Oh, I really do like that show! It's not accurate, of course, but it's done some wonderful things for mankind's consciousness! Well, for one thing," she added when I looked at her in question, " At least for one hour every week, it causes millions of people to focus on the wonders of God, and then, just Andrew alone! Wow...now that's a handsome angel of death! SOOOOOOoooooooo much better than the ghastly, morbid creature that has been instilled from the "Scrooge" image!" She looked ready to prattle on, so I thought I'd better rescue her from another "tangent."

29

"But, you don't fly, or mysteriously disappear and appear at will?"

"Oh, no...in physical terms I'm as ordinary as any human. I mean, in that sense, I can't even be called an angel at all!"

"Why is that? Why can't you do anything like that, if you're an angel?"

"Quite simply, it's the limitations of the physical body, and I agreed to take on a physical body. I was born into flesh just like everybody else, and I will leave this flesh when it dies just like everybody else. The only difference between myself and other human beings is that I remember from where I came. I am in touch with my heart. I am able to have communion with God daily. Not just talk to God, but BE in that presence, feel the love that IS, know I am held in the heart of hearts forever and ever." As she said those words, her eyes closed and I felt a change in the energy around us. There was definitely a change of energy about her, and her face did seem to take on a glow. I was somewhat overwhelmed and uncomfortable by the intensity of the moment and wanted to break that intensity.

"You told me you couldn't glow. You just glowed."

She opened her eyes, "Don't tell me I glowed like Monica and her cohorts do."

"It was nothing like that." I responded. I was suddenly nervous around this woman, because I had observed carefully what had taken place with her, and now I was starting to believe she might be who she had claimed to be. "There was a change..." I faltered. I didn't know how to describe what I had seen. For lack of words, I starting describing what it was not. "You know, on TV, when Monica "lights up," you can tell that she is hit with a spot light. The light comes from above and behind her.

But just now...it seemed like...I don't know...it came from inside of you, to out.   It wasn't like this bright light that's easy to see...it was...very, very...soft..." I shook my head in frustration. "But clear. I could clearly see...a light...kind of blue white..." That was it; I stopped and gave up the struggle. I looked over at her and was startled to see her with her eyes closed again. There was a beatific smile on her face, and she was shining.

"Yes," she said softly. "It comes from within. There is a place inside of me where God and I can touch one another, and know that we are in communion together." She opened her eyes, "And it's not just inside of me, it's inside of you, and every single person on the face of this earth."

"I? I could do that? I could do what you just did? No." I said in denial. "I can't do that. I've never done anything like that. You can do it because you're an angel."

"Yes." She said it emphatically as she opened her eyes. "Yes, you can. " She got up, walked over to me and took me by the shoulders.   "Susan, look at me," she commanded, and then suddenly I was caught by the power I saw in her eyes. "God created all of us. He loves us all equally. He has never shut the door. All it takes is for you to open yourself to Him. Don't you see? This is why I'm here. This is why all the thousands of angels and souls have come here to earth. To point the way. To let it be known that God is calling to us: "Remember me! I have not forgotten you! Come home to me! I love you, I love you!"

I pushed her away from me and stepped back. I was suddenly scared of her. Maybe she *was* going to throw me over a cliff. She knew she had frightened me and apologized. "Please, don't be afraid of me. I could never

31

harm you," and then suddenly she laughed! "And I certainly didn't come here to accost people like I just did you and shout God's message at them like that. Man, oh man," she continued laughing at herself for a moment and then said the most frightening thing of all. "No, I don't want to do any shouting. I'll let you do it for me."

"Me!" I exclaimed, "You want me to shout your message?!"

"No," she corrected, "I want you to write God's message."

"Are you telling me you want me to write a book?"

"Well, you did tell me when we first met that you wanted to write it all down anyway."

"Whoa, whoa, whoa, wait a minute!" I commanded, feeling like the world was whirling around me. I sat back down on the big boulder, because now I was thinking I wasn't going to be thrown off the mountain, I was just going to fall off. And I felt like I already had. I stared in stupefaction at the beautiful vista I was viewing but no longer seeing. All the thoughts in my head had just shattered and blown away. I grasped at anything. "A book. A book. You want me to write a book. I go out hiking on a mountain and I meet an angel named Solomon who wants me to write a book? This cannot be happening to me. Yep, this is crazy." I jumped up from where I had been sitting and started down the ladder.

"Where are you going?" Janet called after me.

"You meet me; a complete, total stranger and tell me you want me to write a book. Where does it look like I'm going? I'm leaving. This conversation is over."

"You don't have to write the book," she said softly.

I stopped, popped my head back up over the rock and looked at her. "What?"

"I said," she repeated, "You don't have to write the book."

"I don't?" I said warily. Now, I didn't trust her as far as I could spit. I figured she was out to trick me and I was going to be very careful here. I was not about to agree to something I was sure I didn't want to do. I still stood on the ladder, ready to make my descent if need be.

"No, no, no, please. Re l a x. Come back. Please. Just take a moment to relax. I am not demanding you do anything. God is not demanding you do anything. If you should decide you do not want to write this book, it will be perfectly okay. It will be fine. Do you understand? It is totally up to you. It is whatever you feel like doing. Please just come back and sit."

"And what if my answer is no?"

She shrugged. "I will feel sorry that an opportunity was lost, then I will seek another."

I came back on to the rock. "That's it? You'll just 'seek another?' I'll be free to go my merry way with no retribution?"

"Absolutely! You think God would punish you for saying no!?"

"Well, I don't know...I've never been in this type of situation before."

"Nothing in your life will change. You will go on just as you always have."

I noticed when she said that, that she looked somewhat sad. I knew it! I pounced.

"There! Manipulation! You looked sad when you said that. You did it deliberately."

She looked even sadder. "I'm sorry."

"Would you stop doing that? And why are you looking like that?"

33

She shook her head and apologized again. "I'm sorry. You're right. I have no reason to look sad. If you decide not to do the book, there is absolutely nothing at all wrong with that. Nothing. It's just that...."

"I knew it!" I pounced again. "Here it comes. Let me have it!"

She sighed. "Alright. But would you please just relax? Nobody is going to force you to do anything. Okay?"

"Alright," I said, feeling somewhat mollified, "Go ahead."

"Think about what I said. Nothing in your life will change. You will go on exactly as you have."

"So."

"Precisely. You will remain exactly where you are. I find that sad because it's a missed opportunity, that's all."

"I know I'm going to regret this, but explain."

She grinned. "I find you so funny, Grace. You really are delightful, do you know that?"

"Please don't call me Grace and answer the question, alright?"

She smiled again. "Okay. The way it is here is that you are being given an opportunity. The decision to act on the opportunity is yours alone. If you decide the answer is no, so be it. Your life will be the same. No problem right? You have a good life. You're a good person; in fact you're one of those in the twenty-five percent who are spiritually functional. So, it's definitely not bad if you decide to pass on the opportunity. Your life will remain the same. Got it?"

I nodded.

"On the other hand," she continued, "Should you decide to take this opportunity, your life will change...in many ways, on many levels. It's an opportunity of rich spiritual growth, new challenges to overcome. You will

34

add some zest and enthusiasm to your life again. It will pave the way for even more opportunities of growth. The potentials are endless."

"You didn't say anything specific here. It was all generalities."

"Hey, we're talking about future possibilities here. You make your future, and I don't do fortune telling. I do have a question for you though." I nodded my head and she continued. "You did say you were going to journal our conversation today, isn't that right?"

"That's right," I agreed reluctantly.

"Okay, tell me something. If you journal your experiences everyday while you are here, what will you have at the end of the week?"

"My journal." I said defiantly, "The same as I've always had."

"That sounds like an answer," she said and sat back down for a good view of the mountain scenery, "Is it?"

"Yes, it is," I said, still being obstinate on principle. "I've decided the answer is no."

"Okay. Did I finish telling you the analogy on how I took embodiment? I don't think I did. I remember leaving off...where did I leave off? Oh yeah...I was saying that we were warned that by taking embodiment we would more than likely..."

I interrupted. "That's it? Okay? That's all you're going to say? You're not going to try to convince me it's the right thing to do?" I had a "bee in the old bonnet" all right.

She rolled her eyes to heaven, "Dear God, I have a person who has said no to us, and now wants us to argue. Save me." She then cut her eyes to me. "No."

"Really?"

"Really." She looked at her watch. "Look, it's 4:00 PM, and the park likes everybody to be off the mountain by six. Why don't you just let me finish telling you the analogy, then we can go our separate ways. Does that sound good to you?"

Well, there wasn't much I could say to that. I had said I wasn't going to write the book. Why waste more time with me? I was interested in hearing the last of the analogy so I told her to go ahead. I sat back down on the boulder next to her and waited for her to start.

"As I was saying before, we were told we would more than likely forget who we were in the birth process. We would still have our connection to God, but no memories. I know," she answered my unspoken question, "While I do have the memory of who I am, I didn't start out from the time I was born remembering I was an angel. It was a process that I grew into. The original plan given to us by God was first, that we should be born and live a life of example. The souls and angels who agreed to take on this task are all around the world. If we continue to use the example of a spiritual army, each continent on the Earth has the equivalent of, let's say a five-star general. Each one of these people were born and then either gradually came into their knowing, or opened suddenly through a spiritual enhancement. Each of these so called five-star generals then has his or her captains and lieutenants who work with him or her on various spiritual projects. The main function of all the thousands who come here is to live a spiritual life; to be an example of LOVE in action."

I noticed she didn't look too happy while she was giving me this information, so I said, "So, what's the problem? Did something go wrong?"

She sighed, "To say something went wrong isn't exactly correct..." she paused and stared off into space for a minute before continuing. "The energies here are so dense...and when it came time to activate...so many couldn't remember and the truth is...we really could have used even more volunteers." She paused again, then said, "Free will caused its problems for us as well. A number of us made some bad choices and really didn't appropriately prepare ourselves."

"But you did okay, right? I mean, you just told me that you grew into knowing you are an angel, so, I guess you did things correctly."

"Not entirely, " she answered. " I made a few fall-flat-on-your-face decisions that could have cost me my assignment."

"No kidding? So you might have been a real life fallen angel, huh? What did you do wrong?" She nailed me with her gaze again, and I was sorry I asked. I saw such deep pain there that I felt immediate contrition for my nosiness. "Never mind." I altered my question, "So, if you came so close to messing up, how did you get straightened out?"

At that question, she obviously brightened. "Well, despite the fact that I slipped on the old proverbial banana peel a few times, my heart always had good intentions and," she paused and her face lit up as she finished, "I received some help from a friend."

"A friend?"

She lifted her eyes heavenward and smiled lovingly, "A very good friend." She stared into the peaks of the mountains for a moment and then once again focused her gaze on me. "As an angel, before taking embodiment into human form, I was nothing more than a projection of Light, straight out of the heart of God. When I was not needed by God to be a messenger, I returned to him and rested again in the heart, becoming one. I had no free will of my own. There was no need to have, or any desire to have, free will. Once I took embodiment, however, I was given the gift of free will as every human being is given it. Free will is the power to create, the freedom to make decisions on your own, the ability to create for yourself what you want to experience in this lifetime. God will guide you, but will never interfere with that which he has given. As a matter of fact," she laughed shaking her head, "I would give it back to him gladly, but he absolutely insists that I have it while I'm on the earth!" She jumped up and brushed gravel from the seat of her jeans. "Well, I guess we should head back before they close the park."

"But you haven't finished telling me how you took embodiment." I objected.

"Oh, I did really. I was born into this physical body, grew up, here I am." She started crossing the boulder back to where the wooden ladder would start us back down.

"You're being very flippant," I said following her.

"No, I'm not," She said, then amended. "Well, I'm not trying to be. It's just that we've run out of time here, and you've already told me you don't want to write a book, so, I guess there's no need to go further than I have, is there?"

" I guess not," I agreed.

We went down the ladder and started back on the path that would lead us down to the parking lot and store where the swinging bridge is located. We came to a place on the path where a person can go one of three ways: one, keep going further across the mountain range; two, go back down the way we had originally ascended; or three, go down the mountain on an entirely different path through a forest canopy. At that stopping point she turned to me and stuck out her hand to shake mine. I reached out and as we shook hands she said, "It was a pleasure hiking with you today. If you don't mind, I'd like to go different ways down the mountain, because I'd like a little time alone."

I nodded my head. "Look, I'm sorry, but I just don't feel..." I began, but she interrupted.

"It's alright Susan," she said soothingly and then repeated, "It really is alright." Her voice was gentle and her smile warm. She put both hands around my one then looked squarely in my eyes. "God bless you," she said, holding my vision for a moment more. She dropped my hands, smiled, and turned to go back down the way we had come up.

Since she had gone back the way we originally came, unless I was going to walk further across the mountain, I had no choice but to go down the mountain through the forest canopy. It is a very shady, cool way to go back down, but it consists mainly of an old rockslide. Almost the entire way, one must slowly and carefully climb over, and past, rock after rock after rock. It takes longer to get down the mountain this way, so I knew I had no time to waste. During my entire descent, I thought carefully over everything I had heard. I really just did not know what to think of the information, or of the woman I had met that day.

When I finally got to the parking lot, there were only a few cars left. I wondered if she had beat me down or was still up on the mountain somewhere. It was already past 6 PM, but I was sure the park gave people a time leeway to get back safely. I gave what I hoped was a casual look at the remaining cars to see if there was anything about them that would indicate an angel might be the owner. I was not disappointed and my discovery was made almost at first glance at the first car I approached. Her License plate read, "LOVE1NTR."

CHAPTER TWO

I knew instantly what it meant. "Love one another," I said it aloud. I stood staring at the personalized license plate as the words repeated themselves in my head, and for some reason, I felt a return of the contrariness and anger I had felt earlier in the day. "Damn!" I swore softly and turning away from her car, I got into my own car and drove back to Blowing Rock as fast as I could. I went into the main street area of Blowing Rock and pulled in to the parking area for "Cheeseburgers," one of my favorite eateries. I knew I had a lot of information to get down, so I took my journal inside with me.

I was seated by a tall, red headed young waiter who was probably a college student at Appalachian State, which is just fifteen minutes down the road in Boone.

"Miller Lite," I told him as he handed me a menu.

"You got it," he nodded and dashed off.

I immediately opened my journal and started writing. The red head returned and I popped the bottle top after I gave my order. I sipped on the chilled brew as I wrote.

"Writing a novel?" His words were uttered pleasantly, and I looked up to see the college kid with the food I had ordered. The strength of my irritation at his words surprised me.

"No," I answered, attempting to sound pleasant, "just journaling."

"Oh," he hesitated from my obvious annoyance. He grinned boyishly, as if hoping I was just hungry so he wouldn't lose his tip for the evening. "Here are your eats, enjoy it while it's hot; want another beer?"

I nodded affirmatively, then added, "Make it a bucket."

"You got it," he repeated his earlier words, then went off to get a six-pack of beer, stuck into a plastic bucket filled with ice.

I inhaled the burger, fries and onion rings in front of me. I had eaten no lunch up on the mountain and was now starving. I could think of nothing else that would have tasted better than the fare I was consuming with super speed. I drank one more beer as I continued to write furiously in my journal. I had no intentions of drinking all the beers at the restaurant, but I did intend to take them back to the hotel refrigerator in my room and drink more of them there. My grumpiness and ill feelings continued, but I managed to leave the red head a decent tip for his service, and I drove down to "The Valley View" where I was staying.

I've stayed at this particular motel many times over the years. It's certainly not what anyone would call classy as far as the rooms go, that's for sure. The rooms are ordinary: two double beds, a TV, a small refrigerator, a dresser and a bathroom. Clean and simple, no luxury. But what it does have beats any other reasonably priced motel in the entire mountain area: the view. On the backside of the motel is a cement porch. On the porch have been placed white plastic lawn chairs and a few rockers. Those chairs overlook a view of the mountains where I can sit and watch for hours and often do. At night, when I can no longer see the valley and peaks of the hills, my eyes then turn toward the sky and I am treated to a dazzling display of heavenly starlight. There are no lights from a large city to block the shine of the stars, so they are abundant in display and number. I am particularly awed on the nights when there are meteor showers. Watching a "star" shoot across the sky gives me a major thrill, no matter how often it occurs.

With beer number three, my journal and a tiny book lamp, I went out onto the back porch of "The Valley View," sat in a rocker and propped my booted feet up on the iron railing, while I simultaneously wrote and gazed at the heavens. I finished writing around midnight, then continued to sit there while I finally examined the anger I had been feeling ever since "the angel" had proposed the suggestion of a book.

I frowned at the beer bottle in my hand. Three beers were excessive for me. Drinking anything alcoholic at all was unusual for me. I was normally the classic "social drinker." I did not keep alcohol of any kind in my home and only drank wine or beer when at a restaurant or at a wedding or a large party.

I stayed away from any hard liquor, just on the principle that I couldn't see the point of drinking liquor except to get drunk, and drinking just to get drunk seemed to have no point at all. Having been a police officer and detective for many years, and picking up I don't know how many drunks off the street, re-enforced my stringent drinking habits. The beer bottle in my hand was a sign of my anger. I was still feeling defiant towards the so-called angel, as well as toward God. Why so angry? That was the question I needed to examine. I was feeling a knot in my chest; a constriction that seemed to tighten with each passing moment. I drained the last of beer number three, and like a child sticking out it's tongue, I marched back to the tiny refrigerator in my room and took out beer number four. Back outside, I popped the top then raised the cold bottle toward the starry heavens in a mock salute. "See?" I said mentally, "See me? I said no, and you can't make me!" I brought the bottle to my lips and chugged half the bottle. "You can't make me!" I exclaimed aloud.

I had been drinking the beers over a period of six hours, so it would have been a stretch to say I was anywhere near being intoxicated, but my mind felt stewed, as if I'd had much more than just "Lites." Maybe the altitude level had something to do with it, but suddenly I felt very dizzy and disoriented, and I quickly grabbed for the iron railing to keep from falling. As I did so, the beer bottle in my right hand slipped and fell down into the bushes below.

"Ohhhhh man! Shoot!" I exclaimed and leaned over as far as I dared, peering for the bottle. I hadn't heard it break, so that was a good sign, I thought. There was no question about me going down and getting it, only because of the disdain I carried for litterbugs. I always took great care to re-cycle and do away with litter properly, and I certainly did not want to garbage an area I thought of so highly. In a childishly irrational way, this incident fed my anger at God. "This is your fault," I grumbled, "I wouldn't have been drinking this beer anyway, if you weren't trying to interfere in my life." Back in my room, I retrieved a flashlight, then made my way down the back stairs to ground level, then to the place where the beer bottle had fallen. I moved as quietly as I could, now that it was approaching 1 AM and I did not want to awaken anyone sleeping. I noticed however, that the night sounds were quite loud. There were frogs croaking, crickets sawing, and the whirring of bat wings as the creatures chased the numerous flying bugs. I could have stomped as hard as I wanted and not been heard through the night sounds going on around me. Still, I moved cautiously. It felt spooky out there in the night on the mountainside.

When I reached the place below the balcony of my room, I panned the bushes and brush for the fallen beer bottle. I swore quietly when I finally saw it. "The Valley View" was perched on quite a steep hillside, and the bottle had rolled down to where I would have to venture off the banked side and down into the slope to get it. I hesitated, now wondering if I should just leave it there...I mean, what was one beer bottle after all? My conscience nagged me forward, "Only one beer bottle! Yep, that's just what every other litter bug tells himself when one goes out the window!"

I shined the light on the bottle again. It wasn't too far, only about five feet down the slope. I was going to get scratched though; there were nothing but thorny blackberry bushes on the sides. I should have put on long pants. Just five feet. I gingerly stepped off the side, trying to avoid the thorns as best I could. After a couple of feet, I crouched down and tried to reach for the bottle stretching out as far as I could, and lost my balance, tumbling sideways down the hill.

"Yiiiiiiiiiii!" I yelped as bush after bush flayed me in passing. Fortunately, I rolled down only about 10 feet before landing square across one of the blackberry bushes, caught in the thorns like a bug in a spider's web. I have to admit that I quickly went beyond polite swearing into the hard core phrases I had learned when I had been a police officer. I won't share them; suffice it to say that what came out of my mouth would have burned the ears off a young child. I was crying too, sobbing like a baby. I blamed the whole scenario on God. "@#**#!! God! This is all your fault! I said no, #@#8! and look what you did! Oh, ##&*#!!" As I cried and cursed, I ripped myself out of the bushes and tramped back up the hill as best I could, still managing to grab the offending beer bottle on the climb back up. I no longer cared if I woke anybody as I made my way back up to my room, but apparently my short yelps and cries had gone unnoticed in the sounds of the night. Nobody came out of his or her room and I was grateful that I didn't have to suffer embarrassment on top of injury. I was quite thankful that I still had on my hiking boots when I had gone down, so when I fell, there were no injuries to my feet and ankles. My calves, knees and lower thighs were a different story altogether, as were my forearms, wrists and backs of my hands. Any exposed skin was now a mass of long burning scratches. My face didn't fare as badly, because when I slipped, I had immediately slapped my hands over my eyes to protect them from lashing thorns. I also had a bleeding scalp where tufts of hair had been abruptly removed. Literally, I was not a happy camper.

I went into my room and after locking up, I peeled off the remaining shreds of clothes and got immediately into the shower. I soaped every inch of myself despite the intensification of the burning pain. There was an interesting element to the physical pain I experienced. As bad as it was, it didn't seem to feel any worse than the emotional knot I had experienced earlier, and somehow, dealing with all of it caused me to see the emotional pain for what it really was. It hadn't been anger I was feeling, it was fear. Standing there in that shower, covered from head to toe with soap, I knew exactly what was bothering me about the day's events. I was afraid! I was afraid of the changes that might occur in my life if I wrote and published a book about an angel who had spoken to me. I had a comfortable life and I didn't want that to change. Why? Was I afraid that change would be bad? I guess so, or else it wouldn't have scared me as much as it did. Then I laughed out loud. Whoever said that if I wrote a book that anybody would ever want to publish it anyway? The chances were better that even if I sent it to a

publisher, they wouldn't want to publish it in the firs
place. I was probably perfectly safe in agreeing to th
angel's request and putting all the information she gav
me into book form. After that, I should just take it on
step at a time.

As I was stepping out of the shower, a thought hi
and I stood there dripping all over the floor, frozen ir
mental turmoil. I had already told the woman I woulc
not write it! The deed was already finished for me. Th
opportunity that she had spoken of had already passec
with my negative stand! Regret struck me like a slap ir
the face and mobilized me again. I dried myself, ther
applied an anti-bacterial ointment to the scratches.
didn't try to cover them, there were too many; besides,
figured air-drying would promote faster healing anyway
As I finished getting ready for bed, I wondered if it wa:
possible to find Janet again and ask for anothe
opportunity. I knew my chances were slim; who coulc
know where she might be the next day? "I found her nea
the swinging bridge today," I mumbled outloud to myself,
"maybe I should go back there again tomorrow." I
resolved to do that, and then had another thought tha
made me pause. Maybe I should try and pray. Maybe I
should try talking to God and ask God to give me another
chance.

Uneasiness centered into my stomach again. Praying
was something that I was not really familiar with
anymore. Oh, I believed in God all right, but I had not
been in a church in years. Although I was familiar with
The Lord's Prayer, talking with God on a one-to-one,
personal basis was not something I had done since I was
young. Then I remembered one of the things Janet had
said. She had told me I was one of the twenty-five
percent of people who WAS still spiritually functional. I

wondered how that could be? I certainly did not consider myself religious by any means...if I were to call myself anything it would be...a liberated Methodist. Liberated because I had never agreed with many of the church philosophies, and that was why I had stopped attending church as an adult. But I had always considered myself a good person. I did believe that Jesus was the incarnated Son of God, and had always tried to adhere to what He had taught, even if I did not practice the formal Christian rituals involved. "Maybe," I thought, "Maybe if I ask..." I didn't even finish the sentence in my head.

Now having decided to pray, I felt at a loss on how to start. I drew on my upbringing for help. I remembered that we would often kneel to pray, so in front of the bed, I knelt on my knees and crossed my fingers in front of me. I closed my eyes. Opened them. That closed-eyed thing was distinctly uncomfortable. I looked around the room as if expecting a spiritual apparition to appear. Everything was normal. I closed my eyes again and immediately felt as if someone was hovering close! I opened my eyes again. It would just have to be an open-eyed prayer. I could at least bow my head and stare at my hands I thought. I did that. Now, what to say?! For a moment my mind was utterly blank. Then I thought about it some, formulating what it was I wanted in my mind. "Uh, dear God," I began awkwardly. I felt stupid. I got up off my knees; putting my weight on the scratch wounds hurt like hell anyway. Instead, I sat on the side of the bed. Better. I tried again, "Uh.... God?" WHY was this so difficult?! I had to let it go. I threw myself backward onto the bed and put my arms beneath my head, just staring up at the ceiling. I didn't even try to think about it. I let my mind go blank; I didn't even WANT to think about it, I didn't want to think about anything. I immediately felt more relaxed and at peace. That was much better. I continued to just lay there and not think and gradually I completely relaxed, and at some point the words slipped easily out of my mouth.

"God, I was scared today...really frightened. Of what...I'm not sure. I think some of it is because it's you I'm afraid of...or maybe I'm really afraid of myself. I don't know. I'm confused, God. I do know that I'd like to be given another chance at this opportunity...if that's still possible. I don't know why your angel thought I'd be a good choice, but I'm thankful. Yes," I said, realizing I was speaking the truth. "Yes God, I am thankful and grateful for the opportunity to serve you in this way, if it's still possible to do so." I decided I needed to be a little more definite about it so I added, "Please, God, if it's still possible, give me this opportunity again, and help me to find Janet tomorrow." I paused for a moment then added, " Thank you God, Amen."

I went to sleep with the lights on.

CHAPTER THREE

I wasn't moving very swiftly when I got out of bed the next morning. That tumble down the hill the night before caused some bruises and muscle strains that I was not aware of previously. I groaned as I rose, then reached for my first aid kit to get the bottle of ibuprofen I kept there. I downed three of them dry mouthed, then drank some water from the bathroom sink for good measure. As I dressed, I started formulating plans in my mind for the day, and decided the best way to start was with a good breakfast. It was already close to 8 AM, so I decided to go to Ham's on 321 south. I took my journal with me so I could write down my encounter with the blackberry bushes while I was eating.

Generally, I would eat a large breakfast, skip lunch while hiking, and then eat a big dinner after I finished hiking for the day. I always took plenty of water with me when I hiked, and would throw in a pack of peanut butter crackers in case I got really hungry. When I got to Ham's, I ordered over easy-eggs, grits, bacon, toast, orange juice and coffee. As soon as the coffee was poured I started writing in my journal and I continued to write with the delivery of my feast.

The whistle was soft and low in my ear. "Grace! You really take self flagellation to the extreme, don't you?"

I looked up to brown eyes twinkling in amusement.

"Blackberry bush, Solomon." I responded, emphasizing her name with sarcasm.

"Ooooooh, when you beat around the bush, you really beat around the bush, don't you? Actually," she amended, as she slipped into the seat across from me, "it looks like the bush beat you. Mind if I join you for breakfast?" She asked, then without waiting for an answer she waved to a nearby waitress.

I stared at her while she gave her order, then, when the waitress had gone, I spoke. "You know, I was going to go looking for you after I finished eating, but you found me. How did you do that?"

"I didn't come looking for you," she corrected, "I came in here for breakfast and just saw you sitting there writing in your journal, so I thought I'd come over and say hi."

I raised my brows in skepticism. "After what you told me yesterday, I don't believe it was just coincidence."

She shrugged as a cup of coffee was set in front of her, then she took a moment to add sugar and milk. After taking a sip from her cup, she answered. "So, you want it straight, do you?" I nodded and she continued. "The truth is, I did not consciously come in here looking for you this morning. Really, I didn't. When I left my hotel this morning, I was only looking for a place to eat. As I was driving by this place, however, I got the word to turn in."

"Got the word?" I repeated.

"Yeah, or another way to put it is 'the knowing'. Remember yesterday when I said that communication with words only occurs here in the physical? Well, I received the communication, or another way to say it is that all of a sudden, I knew. I knew this place was where I needed to be, so I drove in and here I am and there you are. That's all."

"But how," I pressed, "how did you know?"

She put her coffee cup down and lowered her head for a moment as if listening. "How do you describe the knowing?" she murmured softly. After a moment, she started speaking rapidly. "Let's back up to where I was in my car about one block before this place, alright? I'll break it down for you bit by bit, since that's the way you want it."

That was, indeed, exactly the way I wanted it, and I nodded, eager to hear what she would say. "As I was driving down 321 South, about a block from here, I suddenly felt a sensation here and here," she said, first touching the top of her head and then her chest where her heart should be. "I would describe the sensation as first, a slight vibration touching me in those two places. Understand that the vibrations first occurred from inside, then expanded outward. Also, there was the sensation of warmth, along with the vibration. I am, as you can understand, quite familiar with this sensation. I know it to be the physical manifestation of my heart to heart connection with God. Next, there was this overwhelming sensation of His love for me and along with that, the sudden information in my mind that this place, Ham's, was a place I needed to be. Period. There were no words attached to it," she told me as I continued to stare at her in expectation. "It wasn't like God spoke and said, "Turn in here, now." It wasn't like that. But I did know what I was supposed to do, so I did!" She picked up her coffee cup and resumed drinking.

"So when you came in here, what were you expecting?"

"I wasn't expecting anything," she answered, "I was simply doing what I had been asked to do." At this point the waitress returned with her breakfast order. We both ate our food for a few minutes until I broke the silence.

"I don't understand. You're driving along and you suddenly know that you need to come into Ham's, so you do it, but you never even question why?"

"Oh, no," she answered, chewing some eggs and swallowing. "You've heard the expression, 'why ask why?' haven't you?" I nodded and she continued. "I don't ask why, because I know that as I follow the direction I am given, that everything will be revealed to me as I go forward."

"That's faith." I responded.

"Oh, no," she disagreed. "Faith is believing when you don't have proof of something and you believe anyway. That is truly to be admired, I tell you."

"And that's not what you had today?" I questioned flatly.

"No, not at all. You see," she explained, continuing to eat matter of factly as she talked, "I don't have faith, because I don't just believe in God, I know God exists. That's very different. I commune with God daily. He surrounds me with His love and we are heart to heart."

"I see," I stated, although I actually had no clue as to what she was talking about. Then, because I felt uncomfortable I said, "I was going to look for you today."

"Oh?" She asked, leaning back and wiping her mouth with a napkin. "Well, now you don't have to look, do you?" She then continued without waiting for an answer. "Tell me, why were you going to look for me?"

"You already know, don't you?"

"Well," she paused, "I have a pretty good idea, but I would like to hear it from you."

I felt extremely uncomfortable and for some reason could not look her in the face. My own face was red with embarrassment. I half mumbled, "I changed my mind and if it's okay, I'd like to be given another opportunity to write for you."

I looked up at her when I felt her hand laid over the top of my left hand. Her eyes were shining with happiness. "Opportunity granted." With the touch of her hand and her simple words, I suddenly went from embarrassment to a feeling of happiness and contentment. I felt good about myself. Even my bruises and scratches seemed to hurt less.

"Thank you."

Her smile grew bigger. "Don't thank me, thank God. I already have!"

I laughed and then we both laughed together. At what, I'm not sure. I felt good and happy, and it just felt right to laugh.

We paid our bill then walked outdoors together. As we stepped out the doors I turned and asked, "Well, where would you like to hike today?"

"Actually," she said as she continued to walk towards her car. "I won't be able to hike with you today."

"What?!" I stopped in amazement. "Excuse me, but now I am totally confused. Didn't I just agree to help you write a book?"

"Yes you did." She reached the door of her car and pulled her car keys from her jeans.

"But if we don't spend the day together, what will I be writing about? I thought the idea was to record my experiences on a day-to-day basis."

"That's right." She unlocked and opened her car door.

"Well? Am I missing something here?" I was still standing in the middle of the parking lot where I had stopped when she told me we would not be spending the day together. She looked at me for a moment without speaking, then walked over to me and spoke softly.

"I have a message for you."

"A message?" I repeated.

"Yes," she answered, "now listen carefully." I looked at her intently waiting for something profound.

"You've agreed to write the book, now trust God."

I was disappointed and I let it show. "That's it? Trust God? I was expecting something more...revelatory."

"Ohhhhhh, Grace! Let me tell you, if you trust in God, it will ALL be revealed. Believe me."

"Please tell me you are going to stop calling me Grace, and that I will I see you tomorrow?"

"Yes, tomorrow will be good." She answered half my question, nodding affirmatively. "Why don't you meet me on the Rough Ridge Trail just off the parkway going towards Grandfather Mountain. Do you know where that is?"

"Yes. What time?"

"Oh, time! Don't worry about the time, we'll find each other. See you tomorrow!" She said getting into her car. She started her car then drove out of the lot, turning left. I still stood there in the middle of the parking lot, watching her go, until somebody honked a horn at me so I would get out of the way. I slowly walked over to my Pontiac and stood by it as I mused. "Now what?" I wondered. Unlike Janet or Solomon, I was not receiving any messages, so I finally got into my own car and drove over to Hwy 105 to enter the Grandfather Trail on what is called the Profile Trail.

This path is dramatically different from the ones that lead off from the mile-high bridge. The sheers are not as high, but the trail is quite a rough-cut. I also wanted to push myself and forced a fast pace, which also made me fully concentrate on where I was putting my hands and feet. It was physically demanding, which was exactly what I wanted. The pathway rolled and dipped, and I traveled under a canopy of hardwood trees most of the time. I crossed the Watauga River and stopped there a while, pausing to take off my shoes and socks and let the cold rushing water flow over my feet. I wanted to just enjoy the visages of nature, but as I sat on a flat rock with my feet dangling in the water, I knew I was pretending to myself. I admitted some frustration and I wondered why I had been called upon for a particular task supposedly by one of God's angels, then left alone to wander without direction. I tried to take ease in the beauty of the many colorful wild flowers growing around me, but I couldn't. When I felt physically refreshed, I continued on my hike and made my way up and past the 200 rock slab steps to the Profile View, from where the trail I was hiking took its name. I gazed upon the profile of old Grandfather Mountain and knew that for me, the day had only been a way to pass the time.

I continued hiking until I reached the postmarks indicating a transition into the Calloway Trail, then I turned back around and descended down the same trail. I reached my car just as the sun was going down, and my stomach told me with strong signals that it had waited long enough for food.

On this evening I decided to dine at "The Original Emporium," another favorite place of mine. It's really a spectacular place to eat during the daytime hours, as it is perched on the side of a mountain, overlooking a deep valley. If one is so inclined, he or she can eat outside on an overized deck, which juts out over a sheer drop. By the time I arrived, however, the sun had long set and I allowed the hostess to seat me without asking for preference. I ordered an oriental chicken, stuffed baked potato and sipped on a glass of sparking spring water as I waited. I had no plans to drink the way I had done the previous night and ordered only a second glass of water with my meal. Afterwards, I went back to the Valley View and as I did the previous night, sat out back in a rocking chair with my feet propped on the railing, gazing at the stars. I felt strangely restless, again not knowing why. I tried to analyze the way I felt, but could only figure out that I was waiting for something to happen...and I was having trouble with the waiting.

There were no beers this night, nor did I have any encounters with the blackberry bushes. I simply rocked and rocked and gazed at the galaxy above me.

Shortly after midnight I decided to go to bed. Sleep came easily as I slipped into dreamless oblivion.

I was suddenly wide-awake. I opened my eyes and looked over at the glowing numbers of the clock/radio sitting on a wall stand between the two double beds. It was 3 AM. I sat up. "What? Is someone here?" I asked. My impression was that I had been awakened, as if my name had been called. The room remained silent. I was alone. The only sounds I could hear were the sawing of the crickets outside and the hum of the small refrigerator in the right corner near the front door. I continued to listen for a moment more, then lay back down, staring into the darkness above me. I crossed my arms beneath my head, lifting my head a bit from the flat pillow. I no longer felt sleepy, but I felt very relaxed and my mind was quiet. At that point, a very odd thing occurred.

Without my direction, or any thought that I should do so, my hands and arms seemed to move as if directed by a different body. I watched in puzzlement as my arms lifted straight up, my hands pointed toward the ceiling, and then stayed there without me giving any effort to their endeavor. My instant reaction was to try and pull them back down. I could not. They were locked solid. "What the..?" I thought and struggled harder. I was starting to feel a little fear. I made the attempt to roll over to my side and discovered my entire body was frozen in place. Now I was definitely feeling fear; on the edge of panic. I went beyond the edge when I suddenly felt firm hand clasps on both my hands and wrists. There was nobody there, but I could feel these hands on mine! I tried to scream, but to my terrible dismay, my mouth and voice were frozen and silent. I became terrorized when the hands began to pull and suddenly I realized I was being separated from my body. Physically I could not, but mentally I was shrieking in mind-numbed horror. There was a tremendous, electric roaring occurring in my ears. It sounded like an ocean of static breaking in rushing waves inside my head.

In panicked desperation, I fought those hands holding on to me. I knew I was being pulled out of my body and there was nothing on earth I wanted more than to stay in that comfortable, physical image I knew so well. Scream, after mental scream erupted from me as I twisted and pulled to get away from those hands.

Suddenly, the hands let go. Since my only thought had become my release, I had a moment of relief until I realized I was floating above the bed at the ceiling of the motel room. In horrified shock and disbelief, I stared down at the bed looking at my dead body.

"Oh, my God! I'm DEEEEAAAADDDD!!!!" I put every ounce of my being into that scream, I can tell you. All of heaven must have heard me. "I'm dead! I'm dead!" I screamed it over and over, "Oh, God, I'm dead!" I became a blithering idiot. I pointed at myself, crying and blubbering. "Oh, look at me, I'm dead! I'm dead! I didn't even get to say good-bye to my mother! I'm dead!" Finally, after an eternity of "I'm deads," I was reduced to mere sobbing anguish over my plight, and at that point I slowly became aware of another sensation that was starting to occur. I felt a presence with me. And in that presence, I began to feel an envelopment of the most wonderful feeling of love. The sensation was if my heart was expanding inside of me. I knew without doubt that I was greatly loved. The love was all around me, inside me and part of me. All fear vanished. All I knew was this love. I merged with that love and there was no separation between it and me.

From the instant I felt the invisible hands clasp my hands, time stopped. TIME STOPPED. It probably took less than half a second in our time for the being who grabbed hold of me to pull me out of my body and fling me to the ceiling. From the instant my hands were touched, however, I began existing in a state of timelessness. I was totally in the eternal now. There was no past or future, only the now and the now was eternity. I know using these words does not help in the understanding of it, but I have to try, because all of the events that occurred while I was out of my body would have taken many hours to experience had they occurred in physical time. Everything that took place that night occurred in no time at all. If I look at the events one way, everything occurred all at once. If I look at them from another perspective, each moment was an eternity all in itself.

While simultaneously experiencing this overwhelming love, I also was aware that the presence with me was expressing humor...at me. As a matter of fact, it was almost as if the presence was trying very hard not to guffaw, but not succeeding very well. I was being laughed at because I thought I was dead.

Again, simultaneously, when I began to experience the love, I also experienced the humor and the understanding that the laughter was because I thought I was dead. And with that understanding, came the true realization. Even as I stared down at my supine body, I knew. Of course I wasn't dead! How could I be dead? I was right here! I was thinking, feeling and expressing. "Ahhhh!" It seemed like an explosion occurred in my brain as yet another realization occurred and I had the understanding that there is no such thing as death. What a misunderstanding we have on earth. We think because a person's heart is no longer beating, or because the physical body has ceased to function, that a person is "dead," without life. We cry and mourn for them, when the reality is, they keep right on living! What we think of as death is simply a transition through an open doorway. Then, of course, I also understood that my physical body wasn't "dead" anyway. My hands and arms were still ramrod straight above me, my eyes were closed, but I could see that I was breathing. I looked asleep. The thought struck me that I really didn't look like myself. I sure didn't look like what I saw when I looked into a mirror! But then, I had never been able to see what I really looked like. Mirrors and photographs are only one dimensional, and I was seeing myself from a three dimensional stance for the first time in my life. I decided I ought to take a closer look, since I figured this would probably be my only chance, so from where I floated, I leaned over and took a closer look at me.

What a shock! I would have never been able to pick myself out of a line-up. I was startled to discover that I was actually better looking than I had previously thought. I had actually always considered myself unattractive, so seeing myself this way was a pleasure! Then another thought occurred. There was my physical body and how it looked, but I was right here, floating at the ceiling. What did the "real" me look like? I bent my head and looked down.

I was not prepared for what I saw. I gasped and then began to cry again, this time from viewing overwhelming beauty. I was so beautiful! How can I describe this to you so you will understand what I saw?   First I will use the phrase, fluid colors.   I still retained the shape of a human being, but all I could see of me were bright, electric, fluidic colors.   I had never seen such vividly alive, light-filled colors!   The colors, all variations of the rainbow, seemed to have a life all their own as they moved within.   It was like watching a fireworks display, with all the hues bursting forth at once.   I am not a physical body at all.   The real me is a light-filled, glowing, electric-color being!   The sheer, exquisite beauty of me was overwhelming.   My mind was whirling.   There was so much happening to me that I could not comprehend it all.   I had a half thought that I needed just a moment, just a second or two to clear my head and wham!   I was back in my body!   It was a physical jolt and my body jerked in the bed.   My arms were numb, from lack of circulation I guessed.   I found I was able to bring them down, so I sat up and rubbed them vigorously to get the blood moving again.   No sooner did I get the blood in my arms going, up they went again!

"No!" I shouted, but to no avail.   I had no control as I flopped back on the bed and found myself being pulled out again.   It was no easier the second time around.   I fought just as hard to stay in my body as I did before.   It was terrifying.   When I was again floating at the ceiling, I became more aware of the loving presence and sensed that whoever it was, was just behind me and to the right. I turned to look and was stunned.   I saw an Angel.

This was not the woman I had met on the mountain; this was NOT Janet.   The being in front of me had no physical body.   It was all Light.   After seeing this Angel, I can now understand how we humans put the wings on our figurines and paintings.   Waves of light flowed out from the center of the being. Looking at it, I could just barely make out a human form, but I could not make out any distinguishing features. The light poured forth from where its heart would be and moved out in rippling waves. The waves of light looked wing-like, but were not wings per-se.

If my body of colors had a jaw, it was now dropping to the floor. And I had thought I was beautiful! I am so sorry that my best attempt to describe it is so pathetic. The truth is, words do not exist to describe what I was seeing before me. This Angel was a pure projection of Love, appearing to me as white light in human form. You notice I do not call it he or she. That is because I got no sense of gender from it. Gender can only be applied to creatures of the earth. This was a Light from God. It was neither male or female, nor a mixture of both. It was Light-consciousness.

It began to communicate with me. Here's another tough one to describe, because it did not use words as we know them. We didn't carry on a conversation, although I will break it down into conversation for better understanding. It was if I received whole bubbles of information. It was whole communication, with complete understanding, without the use of words. It was possible because our separate energies were able to touch and merge. With this communication it was impossible to misunderstand anything. We were communicating heart to heart.

I basically received the information that I am a person of pure heart. Religious or not, I am a person of caring compassion, with love for my fellow man. Unlike the woman I met on the mountain who had been able to remember her contact with God, I was informed that regardless of my poor memory, I am one of the thousands of volunteers who have come to point the way to God.

This night was my awakening. Though I was unpublished, my writing ability is one of my gifts and God wants me to write. In order to write, I need a teacher and the Angel informed me that God had sent it, this Angel of Light, to be my first teacher. I was also informed that while Janet is also a teacher for me, she had mainly been brought into my life so that I could have someone to talk with, who would understand and be my friend.

"You will go to schools on the inner levels," the Angel informed me, "I have used tonight to introduce you to a new existence and to me. On following nights, you will experience other things and other places. For tonight, we will concentrate on taking you in and out of your body so you will stop fearing it when it happens."

Instantly, I was back in my physical body. Can your arms be so numb they hurt? Mine did. I was glad to bring them down again so I could vigorously get the circulation going again. As before, the minute they felt normal, I flopped onto my back, my arms lifted and I was then pulled out. No sooner was I out; I was put back in. Then out, then in, then out, then in. This was not my idea of a fun time. I have to liken the sensation to feeling as if I were a piece of Velcro. I have to admit that I don't know what it feels like to be Velcro, but I have held Velcro and pulled the two pieces that go together apart, and that's how I can describe what it felt like to be a part of my body, then pulled apart from my body. Yeah, Velcro. In. Out. In. Out. In. Out. Over and over and over. Finally, after about twenty times, I realized I was no longer afraid. I still didn't like the sensation, but could deal with it. My loss of fear telepathically communicated itself to the Angel and the in and out lesson stopped. I was so relieved.

"If your physical energy had been more refined, the experience would not have been so traumatizing to you," the Angel told me.

"My energy?" I asked. I then received an entire communication regarding energy and its relation to the physical and non-physical universe. I am not even going to begin to attempt to translate what I received in its entirety. The only thing I was asking was what my energy had to do with my being pulled out of my body. What I received was a discourse in astrophysics, beginning with the anatomical make-up of matter! Please understand that astrophysics is not a subject I was familiar with, nor had any interest in until that moment! These "bubbles" of instant information are difficult for me to describe into words and what I am going to tell you is a minuscule portion of what I received.

Basically, I was told that everything is energy. Everything we see, hear, or touch is vibrating energy. Some things vibrate so rapidly we can not see them with the physical eyes. Other things vibrate so slowly, we come to the conclusion they are solid fixtures. Our physical bodies are also vibrating energy systems.

When Earth scientists began their studies of atoms, they discovered that all atoms have a center called a nucleus, surrounded by electrons. The nucleus has a positive energy charge; the electrons have a negative energy charge. The attraction of the positive and negative energies is what holds the atom together. The electrons surrounding the nucleus are in constant motion around the centered nucleus, and in between the nucleus and the electrons is empty space.

In addition to our "physical" body, we have other energy bodies, all a part of our totality. Our "physical" body is our nucleus, with the other energies vibrating in and around the physical body. Within this combined framework of energies is another energy system in which the "physical" body and the "other" bodies interact. They are centers of energies, called "The Chakras", and there are hundreds of them located all over the physical body.

When I was first pulled out of my body and decided to look at the "real" me, what I saw were the colors of my energy system. I am not going to go into details about Chakras. I have learned since I first had this experience that there are literally hundreds of books on the subject, and should you want to know more information on them, there are numerous sources for your research.

The Angel communicated to me that it is very possible and, in fact, easy to increase the vibrations of your physical body's energies. The Angel suggested to me that I take the time to learn some exercises, explaining that as I became more successful in increasing my energies, that I would find it easier and easier to leave my body and move into other dimensions. Since I certainly did not enjoy the sensation I experienced when leaving my body, I decided that I would definitely learn some techniques to increase and refine my energies.

After I had absorbed this information, the Angel informed me that this first night's lessons were over and that it would come again for me the following night. I was then instructed to get back into my body.

Old doubting Thomas reared his head. "Excuse me, but can we wait just a minute here?" I asked. "Now, I know this was a very vivid experience, but I am afraid that when I wake up in the morning, I am going to think this was just some wild dream. I hate to say this, but the truth is, I would really like some proof that all this has actually happened and is not some creative mind thing!"

Two things happened simultaneously. The hotel room disappeared and I felt a sensation of movement. The next instant, I was nowhere near the mountains of North Carolina, but found myself floating outside my parent's brick house in Florence, South Carolina, some two hundred miles away. The Angel was with me and we were at the back right side of the house, just outside what used to be my bedroom when I lived at home. I looked around, recognizing where I was. I looked at the Angel. "So what does this prove?" I asked.

"Go inside."

"Go inside?"

"Go through the wall."

"Go through the wall?" I was dumbfounded. How did one go through a wall?

I don't know if anybody has ever tested the patience of an angel, but I certainly did. I received very exact instructions.

"Move up to the brick. Place your hands on the brick. Push forward on the brick."

I did as I was told. I moved right up to the rough red brick, placing my hands, and even the nose of this energy body right on it. I thought to myself. "Okay, now I push?" Hesitantly I pushed myself forward, and to my absolute amazement, found myself moving into the brick, through the space between the brick and the plaster, and through the wallboards and paint.

When I went through that brick wall, I was able to feel every nuance there is to brick. I experienced every molecule and atom of what makes up brick, in its texture, color, taste, smell and its vibratory sound. I experienced the same with the wood boards, the plasterboards and the paint. It was truly an awesome experience all in itself.

When I made it through the entire wall, I found myself floating at the ceiling. I hadn't talked to my parents in a few weeks and wasn't even sure they were home. I wondered why I was back home in my old bedroom. What would this prove? I was certainly familiar with what my old room looked like with the decorations on the walls, as well as the furnishings. Everything was the same. Oops! Hold on a minute, there *was* something different after all. I peered down at the queen-size bed in the center of the room. There was someone sleeping in my old bed! I looked closer. Sleeping in the bed was my older sister Jan and her husband Dan, apparently visiting overnight from Columbia, South Carolina. "That's odd," I thought, "Columbia is only an hour and a half away...why would they spend the night?" Then I shrugged my "energy" shoulders. Well, so what? So my sister and her husband were visiting my parents. I turned and asked the Angel again, "So, what does this prove?"

"Just call your mother in the morning."

Whoosh! I suddenly found myself back in my physical body, back in the hotel room in Blowing Rock, North Carolina. I pulled my arms down, sat up, and this time got up out of bed. I looked at the clock. It was only 3:20! How could all that had happened occur in such a short period of time?! I was infused with wide awake, nervous energy. I could hardly wait to phone my parents. I knew that if I could verify that my sister and her husband were actually visiting my parents, I would at least have psychological proof that the events of the night were real. I wanted to call then, yet didn't want to wake my elderly parents.

I paced, I tried to write, but couldn't. I finally decided to take a very long shower, and at 5 AM, unable to wait a minute more, I called.

My mother answered.

"Hi Mom," I said, suddenly unsure of how I should word my conversation.

"Why, hello Susan!" she responded, the pleasure of hearing from me evident in her voice, followed by sudden worry. "It's five o'clock in the morning, dear. Is everything alright?"

"Yeah, Mom, fine, fine." I hesitated and she waited for me to continue. "So, ah...Mom, ah...why are Jan and Dan sleeping in my old room?"

My mother gasped loudly. "How did you know they were here?!"

I flopped to my bed hardly able to speak. So it had all been real! "Mom," I managed to sputter, "you wouldn't believe me if I told you."

CHAPTER FOUR

I hate to admit that after I told my mother she wouldn't believe me, I hung up on her. I really didn't realize what I was doing; I was pretty much in a state of shock. More had happened to me than I could comprehend and I was literally walking around in a daze. It was too early to go to Ham's for breakfast, so I forced myself to sit down and start writing what I could remember. There was much that was lost. I especially remembered little of the discourse on astrophysics. This was reasonable to me since my math skills have always existed on the nil level. It's not difficult to understand that any of what I received would not make much sense to me unless I had better understandings of math and chemistry to start with. It's a shame, but that's just the truth of the matter.

I wrote until I felt sure Ham's would be open, then left to go eat. Very little affects my appetite. The only time I have difficulty eating is when and if I get severely depressed, which is rare. When I got there, I ordered my regular breakfast and continued to write as much as I could remember of the night time experience. Every now and then I would look around to see if my new friend Janet had come in. She did not show up this day. I was anxious to see her so I hurried through my meal and left for the Rough Ridge Trail as soon as I finished.

I felt myself relaxing as I pulled into the parking area for the trail. I have a lot of favorite trails around the Blue Ridge Parkway, and this is one I visit quite frequently. It's considered a hike of moderate exertion, the exertion being on the legs. The hike starts easily enough from the roadway, passing under a hardwood forest and crossing over a wide creek via a rustic wooden bridge. Shortly after crossing the creek, however, the path changes and more or less becomes a half-mile climb of steps. Many tourists come to this trail because it has some spectacular views, but only the hardy ones make it to the highest ridge point. Because it was still very early in the morning, I had the trail to myself. I hardly paid attention to where I put my feet as I climbed the narrow path cut from rock, making my way to the highest point. When I reached the ridge-sheer, I climbed out on the rock and sat, looking out at yet another face of old Grand Father Mountain. My mind was in overdrive and I sat there for a long time staring into empty space.

"Very, very good," she spoke from behind me, "You're a natural, you know."

I turned to her with relief. Finally!

"You won't believe what happened to me last night!"

She laughed and sat down beside me. "I won't believe you? Are you speaking to somebody else?"

I wasn't in the mood for levity. I continued. "Is this what you meant when you said I was being given an opportunity? I thought I would be getting all the information from you. I never dreamed of this!"

"Did I say I was going to be giving you dictation?"

"Well, no! But, I mean, it was unreal! Bizarre! I just don't even know what to think! I've never, never experienced anything like that! I never expected that!"

She leaned back away from me, giving me a quizzical look. "You've NEVER experienced anything similar?"

"No way!" I shook my head emphatically. "I was pulled out of my body! I saw an Angel...an Angel of Light!"

"You want to tell me all about it?"

"I am DYING to tell you about it."

"Oh. Well, don't die, just tell me."

Another thought suddenly occurred to me. "Wait a minute!" I leaned forward and stared intensely, "That...that wasn't YOU last night was it?"

"Did it look like me?"

"No! I didn't think it was you, but you did tell me you are an angel!"

"I think we ought to use the word "was," Susan. I also told you that within the confines of physical existence, I am just as limited physically as you. No, no, that was your very own Angel, sent directly to you." She was smiling broadly at me, and it suddenly occurred to me that here, next to me, was probably the one person I knew in the whole world who would listen and believe without question. Since I hardly believed the experience myself, I recognized and greatly appreciated the gift I was receiving. I took a deep breath and then began from the point where I had been awakened at 3 AM. She listened without interrupting, sitting with her chin cupped in one hand. She did laugh from time to time, particularly when I was emoting about being dead. When I finished she continued staring at me without comment.

"Well?" I prompted, wanting to hear what she thought.

"Well what?" she asked.

"Well what do you think?"

"Am I suppose to think something?"

71

This time I let my eyes do the talking, and my eyes told her I thought she could be one of the most exasperating people I had ever encountered. She laughed again, shaking her head at me. "I'm sorry," she said, lightly touching me on my arm. "I cannot resist teasing you just a little, but you can be too serious! Please don't think badly of me; I'm trying to help you to lighten up a little when I do that."

I had no choice but to agree with her. I knew very well what a serious minded person I could be. Not saying, of course, that I don't have a good sense of humor, but more often than not, I see things with more gravity than levity.

"Please don't apologize," I told her. "You're right, and it sure won't hurt me to laugh a little more."

"Good!" she responded with a delightful smile. Then she shook a finger at me. "Be warned then."

"Okay," I answered then went right back to my topic, "so, what do you think?"

This time she gave me a pointed look. "No, no. You don't need to know what I think about it. You don't need to know what anybody thinks about it. What anybody else THINKS about your experience is not important. What you think about it is not important. What I would ask you is, what do you FEEL about it?"

I was starting to feel like a parrot, because I was often finding myself repeating whatever I was hearing. None the less I repeated, "What I feel about it? What do you mean what do I feel about it?" She looked at me without answering so I groped around trying to come up with an answer. "What I feel about it," I said slowly, because the truth was I didn't know what I felt about it. "Awestruck," I suddenly blurted.

She smiled and nodded. "Good."

"It was real wasn't it? It really happened. It was not my imagination, it was not a dream, and it was not a hallucination. It was as real as anything I've ever experienced."

"Do you just think it was real, or do you know it was real?"

Suddenly, I remembered that overwhelming love. I was struck with it, once again feeling totally immersed in it; feeling a part of it. It was a totally unconditional love, with no judgement of me whatsoever, complete acceptance of me for me; seeing me as a perfect, beautiful child of God. Tears welled up and overflowed. For a full minute, I couldn't speak. I looked at my friend, completely helpless, completely mute.

"Now, that's what I call FEELING," she said.

I was then laughing and crying simultaneously. "I've never felt anything like that in my entire life."

"Yes, yes, I know, I know. Now you know what I mean when I say to you, I experience God's overwhelming love for me when we communicate. Now you know."

"Am I going to burst into tears for the rest of my life whenever I experience that again?"

"You'll get better at handling it, but also, it won't necessarily be to that degree in the future, if you experience it again at all. And too, 'The memory of the experience is not the experience,' she quoted from the famous Broadway show "Cats," based on a poem originally written by Thomas Stearns Elliot. "But at least you can experience the memory as often as you wish."

I dropped my head into my hands, first shaking my head and then peeking up at her. "You know, sometimes you are too, too, much."

"Ha!" she scoffed, coming right back at me, "You ought to see YOU from my perspective. Too much, indeed!"

She stood up and stretched. "This place is starting to get crowded now, why don't we go on down, get on the Tanawha Trail and hike towards the viaduct?"

I agreed. The Ship Rock, which is the highest peak on the Rough Ridge Trail, is the focal point for all hikers who climb it. Even though the distance from the parking lot to the Ship Rock is only about half a mile, it is quite a strenuous hike up, and once there, visitors tend to stay a while before going back down. Seldom do hikers go further on the trail, which descends sharply into a beech and ash hardwood forest. For those who do take the trail further, it makes a very pleasant woodland walk. Before long, we found ourselves hiking along the length of a deep valley, passing boulders of gigantic size. For about an hour we hiked without talking, until we came to a roughly square-shaped boulder that was approximately 30 feet high and 60 feet long, pushing out of the mountain like some grand stage. We could not resist the notion to go around to the back of it and climb on top of it.

Naturally we sat on the very edge of it, feet dangling over, looking into the sun-dappled valley of trees. We drank some water and rested, then I broke the silence.

"What did you mean when you first spoke to me this morning and said I was a natural?"

It seems like the one thing I did best around this woman was to make her laugh. She did then, too. "You analyze everything, don't you?"

I felt a hot flush of embarrassment. "Is there something wrong with that?" She had been right. The entire time we had been hiking on the trail, I had been happy not to talk, because I was going over and over in my mind the events of the previous night and the conversation of the morning. Analyzing has always been my way of processing information. I try to see an event from all sides, pick it apart, glean from it as much as I can. I tried to defend myself and explained that to her.

She rushed to assure me. "That's perfectly okay! I didn't mean to offend you, but," then she jabbed me in the side with her finger, "you are SO easy to ignite, I can't resist myself. I'd ask your forgiveness, but I'll probably do it again."

I found myself apologizing to her. "I'm sorry to be so defensive. I'm feeling very emotional over what happened to me last night and apprehensive about what is going to happen next. The Angel did tell me it would be back again tonight, and despite all the lessons I had going in and out of my body, I still feel very nervous about it. I feel my world has been turned upside down and on the inside I actually feel like I've been shattered into a billion pieces. I'm no longer the same. I don't know who I am now. I feel like somehow I need to take those pieces and put them back together, but I'm frightened because I know that once I'm altogether, I'll be somebody I don't know."

"Are you sorry you had the experience?"

"Oh no! It was the most wonderful thing I've ever experienced!"

She nodded then reached over, put an arm around me and gave me a brief warm hug. "I'm here to help you as you go through this."

I felt emotion choking my throat again. "Thanks," I said softly.

She brought her hands together in a large clap. "Alright! You want to know what makes you such a natural and what it is you are so natural at, yes?" I nodded and she continued. "First, let me say that you, my friend, are a walking paradox."

" I guess you're going to explain what you're talking about?"

"Yes! You're like a coin, with two opposite sides; like, for instance, Susan on one side, Grace on the other. It would seem one side would negate the other, but it doesn't."

"You don't have many friends, do you?" I asked dryly.

Once again she shouted with laughter, then went on. "Okay, here we go. Side one: You'll admit to me that you're a most analytically minded person, right?' I nodded affirmatively as she continued. "Yes, Susan, you analyze everything. You THINK all the time; you like being in your mind. That's a comfortable place for you." Again I nodded. " Alright. We agree on that. Now for side two, and this is what causes the paradox..." She paused for a moment, looking at me intently. "I don't even know if it's a good idea to tell you this, because knowing about it could possibly spoil it for you." She paused again and I could tell she was waiting to see if she was going to receive communication warning her not to tell me this information. Apparently it was an "all go," because she then continued. "You are a natural meditator. Without effort of any kind, without even thinking about it, which must be the key, you can go into a natural prayer state. You can switch from an analytical mind to an open, non-thinking state of being. It's a state that we could describe as...one of Grace." She stopped and looked at me to see if I got her point, then kept on. "It's a pretty amazing feat, seeing how there are hundreds and thousands of people who make the attempt to meditate everyday and are unable to because they can't stop their mind process. You have done it all your life and haven't even realized you're doing it!"

"I must not realize I'm doing it, because I don't know what you're talking about!"

"That's right, that's what has made it such a crazy, perfect, paradoxical sort of accomplishment. You do it naturally, sort of like the way you breathe. I think that you'll know what I mean when I give you an example of what I'm talking about. You were doing it this morning when I first came up to you on Ship Rock. You were staring off into the distance, your eyes on Grandfather Mountain, but I'd bet you anything that you weren't seeing the mountain at all."

"Oh yeah..." I said slowly, with sudden insight. "I do know what you're talking about. I've never thought of it as meditating though; more like...." I broke off, suddenly thinking of my six-year-old daughter and how she liked to catch me in those types of moments. "My daughter, Jana, tells me I'm in space."

"Ah...smart daughter you have."

"But I still don't understand," I continued. "You say I'm in a meditative state when I'm in this space? Now, this is strange because I've never analyzed my doing that! But if I look at it now, I'd just say I'm zoning out...you know?

"I told you, you're a walking paradox, and every word you've just said proves it."

"But I'm not doing anything when I do that, I just sort of...go off!"

"M'mm, h'mm."

I was getting frustrated again and I repeated, "But I don't DO anything! I'm not thinking about anything, I'm not pondering over some great wisdom, I'm nowhere! I'm just...out there."

"Exactly," she said pointedly. "Now, tell me something. You say you've never analyzed your doing that, but I want you to think about it carefully right now. Take a moment to look at what it is you do, then I want you to tell me what it is you do experience when you're in that place."

So I thought about it. I got up from where I was sitting and I roamed over the top of the boulder. I walked over to the back wall where the earth was exposed, and green ferns and moss grew out of the cracks between the rock. I placed my fingers on the moss and felt its velvety texture. I recognized the paradox. How could I use my mind and analytically pick apart a place where I had no thought? Or, when I was in a place of no thought, how could I think about it when in it? It couldn't be done, could it? If I could think about it, then it wouldn't be happening. I could also see why she had been reluctant to tell me what I had been doing naturally. Would I still be able to do it naturally, when the very process had been because I didn't think about it? Could I think about it now and then just do it? I tried to move into the zone. Failed. She was right; knowing about it made it more difficult for me to do. I recognized that I was way into my left-brain, analytical mind and felt again a knot of frustration forming because I wasn't going to be able to answer her.

"You need to relax!" Her voice floated over to me from where she was sitting. "You're trying too hard. Just stop for a minute." She got up and walked over to me. "Let's get down from here and go find a place where you can sit against a tree, or lay down in some soft grass. You're tense, you're agitated over last night, and the conversation we've been having hasn't helped you relax . Let's just go find a place where you can lay back and relax."

That sounded good to me, so I said okay and followed her off the rock. We continued hiking until we came upon Wilson creek. There were nice, lush patches of grass fairly close to the creek and we sat down. She took command.

"You mind if I do a little relaxation technique with you?" she asked, as she opened up her backpack and took out a soft, blue cotton sweater.

"Do you mean like hypnosis?" I asked, very curious of what she had in mind.

"Sort of," she responded, "But I'm not planning on making suggestions to you, like you see in staged hypnosis routines. I'm just going to try and help you relax and feel more comfortable about yourself, and also help you remember a little better."

"I don't mind that," I told her. "When I was a police detective, the police department sent me to a class on hypnosis so that I could use it for that very thing. I would use it from time to time on witnesses who were having trouble remembering what they had seen at certain crime scenes. It was often a very effective tool."

"Good!" she said, then started right into it. "Take this sweater," she said, handing it me. "Lay down and put it under your head and get as comfortable as possible."

"Why don't I get out my rain poncho and lay that on top of the grass?" I suggested, "Then I won't be worried about ants or other insects crawling into my clothes."

She agreed that was even better, so I made myself comfortable in the mountain grass next to a bubbling, chortling stream. The sounds of the water in all its various sounds as it rushed through narrow spaces and trickled in other spots had a soothing musical quality all its own. I found myself relaxing just by listening to it.

"That's right," began my friend, "let's begin by just listening to the mountain stream as it makes it way through the valley. Listen to its soothing song as it tells you to cast away your worries and relax. Hear the birds as they add their beautiful melodies to the sounds of the creek, as they sing to you to throw away your tensions and relax, relax. Listen to my voice, concentrate on my voice, and you will find yourself relaxing, relaxing, relaxing."

Her voice had become very mellow and soft. It was soothing in its gentleness and I did find myself easily relaxing as I listened. There was a gentle touch to my forehead, just between my eyes. "Keep your eyes closed," she told me, "and with your eyes closed, I want you to stare at this spot on your forehead. Continue to stare at this spot and as you stare I want you to concentrate and relax... concentrate and relax all the muscles in your scalp. As you relax the muscles in your scalp you will feel a tingling sensation moving down, down, down." She went next to all the muscles in my face, my neck, my spine, and then she said, "You feel so good, so wonderful, so relaxed; better than you have ever felt in your life...and so wonderful, so good, so relaxed; better than you have ever felt before." She continued in this way, moving from one body part to another, every now and then pausing to tell me how wonderful, how good, and how relaxed I was feeling. It WAS wonderful; it was certainly working, that was certain. I felt like I was floating on a soft cloud, so relaxed I was almost to the point of falling asleep, but not quite...she told me that too.

She worked her way down to my toes, and by that time I knew I was so relaxed that I wanted to stay in this spot forever and not move. She did not stop there, however. She then told me to imagine that I was standing in a ten-story building, standing in front of shining metal elevator doors. She took me inside the elevator and counted down from ten to one, after every number either saying the word relax, or deeper. When the doors of the elevator opened I found myself in my favorite room at home, sitting and getting comfortable in my favorite easy chair. I was completely and totally relaxed, but knew that I still had enough energy to answer any questions she asked of me. She told me I would be able to remember, clearly and accurately, any events of my past. She spoke to me about my ability to stop thinking, to be in a state of meditation, and asked me if I could remember a time where I first recognized being able to move into that space.

Immediately, with no effort, I had a clear memory of being two and a half years old. I was wearing only my white cotton underwear, sitting outside on the cement steps of our home in Cowpens, South Carolina. It was a bright summer morning and I was sitting there, leaning over, with my chin cupped in both palms of my hands. This vision of memory was so clear that I actually felt I was back there again, as if I were sitting there as the two-year-old I had been. I was back in my two-year-old mind! I remembered these thoughts. "Stare straight ahead, but let my eyes get fuzzy...now...stop thinking." I felt a shifting occur, a raising, and suddenly I wasn't looking through my physical eyes anymore. It seemed as if I was now looking at the world from a higher space, a clearer vision...I was in a place of light and love. I was filled with peace and contentment. My memory continued, as I heard my sister Jan call to me. Jan is older than I am and at this stage in our life she was five years old. "Jan! Jan!" I called back to her, "Come here! I want to show you a fun game!" My sister stepped out the screen door and sat down beside me. "What kind of game?" she asked.

As a two and a half-year-old, I struggled to find the right words to describe the fun I had discovered, so I just gave her the instructions that worked for me. "Stare straight ahead," I told her and she willingly obliged. "Now, let your eyes get fuzzy so things look blurry." Jan attempted this as well. "Have you done that?" I asked, and she nodded, "Okay, now, stop thinking....and.....shift!" My sister rose to her feet in disgust. "What a stupid game! That's not a fun game!" She started to go back inside. I protested, "Oh, but you didn't do it! It IS fun! Try again, try again!"

"No," she said emphatically, "that's a stupid game."

I felt disappointment that my sister had not been able to experience the shift of movement and sensation I was able to create for myself, but did not try again to persuade her. Instead, I simply turned around and amused myself with my new discovery.

Janet broke into my memory. "You have remembered well," she spoke to me in the same calm, soothing voice, "but now it is time to leave this memory and move forward in time. In just a moment I am going to count to three and when I reach that number you will move to a different age and a different memory. The memory I would like you to move to has to do with your being out of your body last night. I would like for you to remember a time in your life where you experienced a similar event...an event where you might now be able to say, 'I was out of my body.' There was a slight pause, then she said, "I am counting now: one, two, three. Tell me how old you are and what you remember."

Vivid memory burst upon me once again. I was suddenly a child again, nine years old, waking up early on a Saturday morning. I watched, as well as experienced again, leaping excitedly out of bed and running down the hallway through the house, then into the kitchen. "Mother! Mother!" I exclaimed, "Guess what?! I can fly! I can FLY!"

My mother, who was cooking breakfast, shook her head and laughed, "Susan! What an imagination you have!"

I ran up to her, tugging on her arm, trying to pull her out doors. "Oh, no, Mother! It's not my imagination, it's real! I can fly! Come outside, Mother. Come outside, I'll show you I can fly!"

My mother pulled her arm away from me and stood where she was at the stove. "I can't go outside right now, can't you see I'm cooking breakfast? You go on, I'll come out and take a look at you in just a minute."

I was in pajamas and I was barefoot, but I didn't stop to put on clothes, I just immediately ran out the back door and into the yard. I lifted my arms to the sky and leaned forward, fully expecting to take off and fly.

Nothing happened. I brought my arms down in puzzlement, then had the thought that maybe I needed to leap up first. I lifted my arms again, then leaped upward as hard and as high as I could. I came back down. No flying. I leaped again, again and again. My mother appeared at the back door and looked out.

"Are you flying?" she asked.

I turned to her in angry frustration. "I don't understand! I could fly last night! I flew all around the trees in the church parking lot and all around the block! I don't understand!" I repeated again.

"Come on in and eat your breakfast," she told me.

I HAD flown the night before. I had gone to bed as usual and for some reason, in the middle of the night, I had awakened. I pushed the covers away from me and sat up in bed looking through the gloom of darkness, then realized I wanted to go outside. I got up, walked through the house, into the den and up to the back door. I paused at the door, looking at it a moment, then just stepped right through it. "Cool!" I thought. I went down the steps into the yard, then looked up at the night sky through the treetops of high pines.   I thought how wonderful it would be if I could fly in the sky and look down from over the top of the trees. I lifted my arms to the sky and before I hardly realized it, I took off into the night sky. I was beside myself with joy and thrilled excitement. "Wow! I must have special powers!" I thought. "I'm like Superman! I can really fly!" I flew over the tops of roofs and checked out the neighborhood, to see how it looked from a sky vantagepoint. I was careful not to leave the area I was familiar with, because I recognized that things looked a lot different from my height and I didn't want to get lost by accident. After a while of flying around in a solitary fashion, I started feeling a little lonely and wished I had a couple of friends to play with. I had this thought as I was finishing a flight around the block, flying low over the sidewalk, coming up to the back of the church parking lot, where my father was the pastor.

In the center of the black asphalt lot, there was a very large, old oak tree that had been left there when the lot was paved. As the tree came into my vision, I saw two children flying in circles around the top of the tree. "Hey!" I called to them and flew even faster to go and meet them.   These were not children I played with regularly. I did not recognize them as being children from the neighborhood. They looked to be about my age, however, and like any child I was ready to quickly be friends and play. "Want to play chase?" I asked.

"Yeah!" they chorused and we took off. Around we went, laughing and yelling; zipping in and out and up and down the trees, the houses and the neighborhood in general. I was having the time of my life. Towards dawn, I realized that it might be time for me to stop the fun and go back inside to bed. I told my new friends goodbye, explaining that I needed to go back in. I then flew back over to my own backyard and landed just about in the spot where I had taken off. I went back inside, once more going through the door and headed back to my bedroom. As I approached the corner where my small, single bed was positioned, I made a running leap; throwing myself onto the bed and was instantly asleep. Waking up from that sleep was when I had run into the kitchen to tell my mother I could fly.

"I am going to count from 10 to 1," Solomon spoke, "but before I do, I would like to suggest to you that you will continue to remember with clarity and accuracy those things you have told me about today. I would also like to tell you that by the count of one, you will be awake and alert, but at the same time mentally peaceful and refreshed."

When I heard the count of one, I opened my eyes and tried to sit up.

"Not too fast," she said, "take your time and move your body around first."

I did as she suggested, starting by wiggling my toes, then stretching fully. I finally sat up. "Wow....." Other words failed me, "wow, wow, wow!"

"Do you hear a dog barking?" she asked and we both burst into laughter.

I guess you'd have to be there, but at the time, it just seemed SO funny! "Wow, wow, wow!" I barked. I laughed until my sides were aching and tears ran down my face. Just when one of us would calm down the other would bark, "Wow, wow, wow!" and off we'd go again. I knew the laughter was a final way of releasing tension and I welcomed it fully. Finally though, when my sides couldn't stand it any more, I begged for mercy. "Please, please!" I gasped, "Please don't bark again!" After we finally settled down, I could hardly believe how good I felt. I was relaxed; there was no more anxiety about the previous nights events, or the conversation we'd been having during the morning. I was ready to do some more hiking and more talking. I looked at my watch. "It's two o'clock. I don't think we can make it all the way to the viaduct then back again before it's dark, but I think we can easily make Yonahlossee Overlook before we turn around. How does that sound to you?"

"Good," she said, jumping to her feet, "let's do it." We started off at a brisk pace and made it there in about 45 minutes, this time talking as we hiked. "So tell me," Solomon asked, "What do you think about your memory retrieval?" Then she added quickly, "Please don't bark again though."

This time I managed to keep my laughter short. "You know, I found the experience when I was just a two year old fascinating. It's easy to see why I would forget teaching myself that process; I was so young! I guess the first time I did it was by accident, then, I guess, as it got easier and easier for me to slip into that space, I just forgot the process and how it started. I can look at it now and recognize that it's something I do when I want to feel at peace. It's a place of comfort and contentment. It really has become a habit that I don't even think about doing. It IS as natural as breathing. I'll tell you the thing that I find most amazing though."

"What's that?" she asked.

"That I could forget my flying experience when I was nine! THAT is what had me barking like a dog earlier. I remember everything about it now. You won't believe the controversy I caused in my family over that!"

At that point, we reached the overlook and I'm sorry to say that we merely took a cursory look, drank some water, then headed back the way we had come. I continued talking. "I remember that the flying occurred every night for a little over a week. On that first day, I remained very puzzled and disappointed for the whole day. But that very next night, it happened again. I woke up, went outside and flew around the neighborhood. After that, I reasoned that I DID have special powers, but that I only had them at night. Being a child, all I knew was that I could fly and walk through doors. It never once occurred to me that I was moving around outside my physical body!"

"What was the controversy you spoke of?" my friend asked.

"Well, this was hot stuff! I was very proud and excited about my special abilities. I went around and told all my friends in the neighborhood and at school that I could fly."

"Did your friends believe you?"

"Oh no, of course not! They all laughed at me. I can remember being so angry because they didn't believe me. I remember standing in a small group and after they laughed and scoffed I said, "You go out there any night! Any night at all, you'll see me!" I told them that I would bring them a leaf from the top of a tree to show them...which is kind of funny to think about now, because how is a leaf from the top of the tree different from one at the bottom? That very night though, I plucked a leaf from the very top of the old oak tree and took it back to my room when I went back to bed. The next morning, however, no matter how hard I searched and believe me, I did search everywhere, I could not find the leaf."

"That's interesting but doesn't sound very controversial; was there more?"

"Oh yes. The trouble started when I started telling people at the church. You know, it's funny. The kids my age, they just laughed and made fun of me to my face. The adults, on the other hand, pretended to believe me, then went to my parents to laugh about me. My parents didn't find it amusing at all. On the second Sunday that I talked about my "special abilities," my parents took me aside for a heavy-duty conversation. This was really serious to my parents because my father is a very respected United Methodist Minister. The very first morning that my flying ability had occurred, both my parents had laughed about my vivid imagination. By the second Sunday, they found nothing funny about it. After church, they both took me into my bedroom, telling me they needed to talk with me. They had me sit on my bed, then my father started talking to me."

"Susan, we understand you've been telling the church members that you can fly," my father said.

"Oh yes!" I responded, "I'm telling everybody, everybody!" I was delighted they were finally talking to me about it and I started chattering away as I had the first morning, explaining to them that I only had my abilities at night, but, oh! how much fun I was having with it!

My mother interrupted me, "But, darling…you can't be going around telling people these stories."

"Why not?" I asked, very puzzled now.

"Because," my father answered very seriously, "you know you can't fly."

"Oh, but I CAN fly!" I said emphatically, then told them what I had said to my friends, "I really can fly! If you go out there at night, you'll see me! I want to show you! I really can fly!"

"I am a Methodist Minister," my father said and he sounded angry. "You are the child of a United Methodist Minister. You cannot be going around telling lies."

At that I burst into tears. They didn't believe me! They thought I was lying. "I'm not lying!" I sobbed. "I'm not lying! I'm telling you the truth. I really CAN fly. Come out there tonight! I can fly! I can fly!"

I believe my parents, at that point, finally understood that I was not lying and that I truly believed what I was saying. They were silent for a moment, wondering, I guess, how it was possible that I could possibly believe I could fly.

"It's a dream!" my mother suddenly blurted out, obviously coming to that conclusion with great relief. My father also seized on that explanation.

"Yes! A dream!" he echoed, then hunkered down so we would be eye to eye. I was still sobbing sadly. "Susan, look at me," he ordered, so I did. When we were looking brown eyes to brown eyes, he said, "Now listen carefully. You cannot fly. It is physically impossible for a human being to fly. I'm telling you, even if you believe it, it is NOT possible. What you have been experiencing has to be a dream." He paused for a second or two to see if I was taking it in, then continued. "I know that you believe that you can fly, but I am telling you that you have been dreaming. It's a wonderful, fantastic dream, but it IS a dream and you cannot physically fly. Do you understand?"

I nodded my head. I believed my mother and father. I mean, after all, they were my mother and my father! They certainly wouldn't tell me something unless it was true! They had to be right and all the flying I had been doing was nothing but a dream.

"I never experienced the flying again," I told Solomon. "It was like slamming a door. I never even thought about it again after that either. I just accepted what my parents said and that was it."

CHAPTER FIVE

After we returned to "The Ship Rock" on the Ridge Trail, my stomach started grumbling so loud, it sounded as if it were echoing off the mountains. I invited Solomon to dine with me, but she once again told me she had other matters to attend to. We decided to meet the next day at the Boone Fork parking area and do some creek hiking along Boone Creek. No time was set, but I was no longer bothered by that idiosyncrasy. I was starting to learn that time, in many ways, was an insignificant detail right now.

I went back to "Cheeseburgers" for supper and proved that I am indeed a creature of habit, once again ordering a large burger, fries and onion rings. With my appetite, the food was more generally engulfed rather than eaten, so it wasn't long before I was headed back to the hotel. I stopped at the Food Lion on 321 and bought several bottles of spring water first, but by 9 PM, I was back at the hotel in my favorite spot, in my favorite rocker, gazing at the heavens.

Since my hypnotic regression earlier in the day, I had not been apprehensive about my upcoming second meeting with the Angel. As it began to get later, however, some prickles of anxiety began to emerge out of my sub-consciousness. I sincerely doubted if there would ever be a time in my life that I would be entirely comfortable feeling like a piece of Velcro, or if there would ever be a time that I could be blasé about standing before a being made of Light? I figured that it would be a good thing to get comfortable as Velcro, but maybe not so good to get blasé on the latter.

My trivial thoughts convinced me that I was simply in standby mode, so, rather than sit out on the porch any longer, I decided to go on to bed. I wasn't the least bit sleepy however, and wondered if anything at all would happen should I fail to fall asleep.

No need to worry on that account! I forgot that I didn't need to be asleep for the action to happen! Even wide-awake, no sooner than I laid down on that bed, my arms rose into the air, and I felt a pair of hands pluck me from my body. I am happy to report that at least this time I was not consumed with overwhelming terror.

Once again, I found myself floating at the ceiling of the Valley View Motel, looking down at my silent, apparently sleeping body. I checked out my "new" duds. Yes, I still had a glorious body of dazzling rainbow lights! "Where is the Angel?" I thought briefly; briefly because I had barely begun to think the question before I was enveloped in all-encompassing Love. I described it before, so there is no need to repeat the words, but how I wish I could express the magnitude of that total, overwhelming sensation of pure love. I would like to stress the word pure here as well. It wasn't love tainted by any human thoughts of romantic passion, or love of a physical expression. It was simple, pure love.

This Being of Light Consciousness was before me again and "told" me that on this night I would again be going to school, but on different levels of vibration. "Tonight you will visit heaven and hell," it communicated. A brief sensation of movement occurred and the Valley View disappeared. A panoramic vision now took its place. I found myself floating in a softly hued blue sky, complete with high thin clouds. Before me, in gently rolling hills of vivid green, were buildings of architectural delight. Now, I know nothing about architecture, but even to my total amateur eye, I could see that all the buildings fit in harmony with one another. Some were domed, others square. They were of different heights and widths, but they all seemed to fit together. There was a feeling of balance and perfection. Oh, and lest I forget the most important detail, it was easy to see, even for me, that they were all made from white light. There was a translucence about them. Quite simply, I knew they were made of light, because they had a transparent glow. It was like somebody, if you can imagine this possibility, took a sheet of white light and folded it into these perfect shapes. They were nestled in groves of trees and flowers, and small, blue water ponds were within easy walking distance from the buildings. "Wow," I thought to myself, "This must surely be heaven. Those flowers! I'd like to get a closer look at those flowers!" Instantly, I was nose to nose with a deeply hued, purple bearded iris.

Now, simultaneously...remember simultaneously? I was getting information from the Angel. It's important to remember that this Angel and I did not carry on conversations like I was having with Janet. I was so in touch with this being, that it was like the Angel knew my thoughts before I even had them. The information I received was total and complete and occurred all at once, so for me the experience was like, "Ahhh! Ahhh! Ahhh!" as complete explosions of information were suddenly there. In order for me to relate any of it you, however, I have no choice but to break it down into conversation, because that is the only way I know to share the experience with you. So...simultaneously, the moment I had the bare thought of, "Wow, this must surely be heaven," I received clarifying information.

Oh, how much easier it would be if I could impart to you the knowledge without having to use words! First, let me say that I received both positive and negative affirmation that I was correct...or incorrect. Yes, what I was experiencing could be called heaven and no, it wasn't. In a general way, it would be called a tiny segment of heaven and it was certainly heavenly, but it wasn't what heaven would be for me. For me, it was simply a place of instruction; school was in session and I was in the classroom.

While I was comprehending this knowledge, I was having a nose-to-nose experience with this incredibly beautiful flower. My eyesight was enhanced; or so it seemed to be, because I could clearly see every cell that made up the iris's biological structure. The velvety looking, ruffled petals were so delicate looking, with a transparency about them. The color! I cannot describe the color! Okay, purple; but it was more than that. All the flowers, not just the Iris I was so closely examining, had color that was more than the spectrums we see on earth. The only description that comes to mind is that the colors were electric! I tried to examine them even closer and saw that I could see into them and that I could see glimmers of light sparkling within each atom. Of course! Like everything here, this flower was made of Light! I felt a desire, and I have to say it was not even a real formed thought, but it was a desire to experience the flower completely, and barely had I experienced the desire than I found myself a part OF the Iris. I experienced the vibratory make up of "Beautiful Purple Iris." I realized that the flower had an awareness of being alive and being a flower. Not the "I Am" consciousness that we experience as human beings, but still a conscious awareness of its place in the universe and its supreme JOY of being!

After a moment, or a millenium, (I'm not sure which it was; remember there is NO time outside of Earth!) I shifted my focus back to the Angel, who had been waiting with eternal patience while I had my fling with the flower.

I would like to add a little more of the information I received regarding heaven before I tell you what I experienced of it.

Once again, we go back to the basics of energy and vibration. There is nothing, absolutely NOTHING that is NOT vibratory. I like the analogy that God is the purest, most refined energy of all, and the more you remove yourself from that energy, the denser, or slower the vibration becomes. Therefore, everything that exists, whether it is a part of "heaven" or "earth," is still a part of the vibratory universe. In that sense, "earth" is not separate from heaven, but is simply a place OF as well. So, we could say we are already in heaven. But since "hell" is also in this vibratory makeup, we could also say we are in hell as well as in heaven.

When Jesus said, "In my house there are many mansions," he wasn't being metaphorical; he was speaking literal truth. Heaven is limitless, and there is an individual heaven or hell for every single person on the earth. The reason that is so is because we each create our own heaven or hell expressly for ourselves, built upon our true belief systems. One thing is for sure; you might be able to fool some of the people all of the time, or some of the people some of the time, but you can never, never, never fool yourself, once you let go of the body. All illusions fade; you will face yourself with blinding naked truth and your "heaven" will be built upon these truths, or lack of them.

I want to clarify that point in order for you to understand that what I ended up experiencing as "heaven" and "hell" could only then be based upon ME and that when it is your turn to experience the "other side," your experience might be similar, or it could be totally different!

While I am speaking of the terms "heaven" and "hell," I guess I should go ahead and mention that it is only on earth that the words "heaven and hell" have meaning. To understand this, I once again have to refer back to the fact that since EVERYTHING is energy or vibration, whether something is "heaven" or "hell" is only a matter of the degree of vibration. Whether it is heaven or hell simply then depends on one's perspective. This means that when one "dies," he or she will then go to that vibratory level to which he or she is ALREADY resonating.

The Angel gave me the choice of which I would prefer to experience first: Heaven or Hell? I decided I would save the best for last and before my "present" environment disappeared, the Angel assured me that because it was with me, I would not be harmed in anyway physically, mentally, emotionally, psychologically, or even spiritually. This was explicit to the point that the Angel did not want me to even experience fear and so told me that it would further blend its energy with mine so that I would view my surroundings within a state of peaceful detachment.

"Whoa..." I communicated back, feeling overwhelmed, "this sounds deadly serious."

I was told that I was going to be experiencing the extreme, or the point of densest energy; somewhat similar in physical terms to the density of a "black hole" that scientists are able to identify in space. The effect that experiencing this energy could have on someone without angelic protection would be devastating. It would be annihilating.

I also understood that I would not be able to experience it completely, because the only way to do so would be without the protection of the angel, and experiencing this energy point without protection would give me the permanent mental capacity of an earthly vegetable. I would be aware that I existed; barely, but no more. I felt very grateful for angelic protection!

When the Angel knew I was ready, the transition to this densest energy point was made. Instead of experiencing overwhelming fear, what I was feeling emotionally was love and peace. Since I described beforehand what would happen to me, without angelic interference, the only thing left to describe is the sensation that was left to me which was touch. What I experienced tactilely I have a great analogy for. The sensation I experienced was that I was emersed in thick, black tar.

When I was a small child of three, a city street crew was re-tarring a section of the road that ran by our house in Cowpens, South Carolina. Late in the afternoon, close to sunset, I walked over to look at the work they had done. On the right side of the street near the edge of the road was a pool of tar that filled what had been a pothole of some dimension. It was approximately three feet long, two feet wide, and had been about a foot deep. I squatted down beside the tar pool and touched the top lightly. It had cooled enough to form a "skin" on top, but was still warm and gooey in the center. Curiously, I decided to stick both hands into the sticky substance and did so; pushing my hands all the way in, until my arms were covered to the elbows. Since I had never experienced tar before, I had no knowledge that the black goo would stick so thoroughly to my skin. I can still vividly remember the shrieking made by my mother when she saw me!

For those of you who have never stuck your arms into tar pitch, I can tell you it's not a real smart thing to do. Tar suffocates the skin, keeping it from breathing, and if I had totally covered myself physically, it would have just been a matter of time before my body died; so, fortunately for me, I had *only* covered my arms. I was also fortunate that the tar was only warm and not still hot. Think of how water feels if it pops on the skin when it is boiling. Can you imagine the damage boiling tar would do? As it was, the only pain I felt was the loss of my skin when my mother jerked me to into the bathroom and used a scrubbing brush to try and remove the tar. It took several weeks before it all came off.

Now, in this place of densest energy, except for a few differences, I felt as though I had jumped into an entire vat of tar. I could hear nothing, I could see nothing. I'm not talking just dark here; I mean a total absence of light. Movement was difficult and slow, just as if I was trying to swim in tar, except it was much denser than that substance. I felt crushing pressure from all points around me and knew that if my physical body had been in this place, it would have been reduced to a size smaller than an atom. It was just that dense. This place not only had an absence of light; it drained the light from anything that came into it. I don't know how long I was there. Even feeling love and peace, I was grateful when I found myself out of that place!

Because I came back from that place with the knowledge that it did away with light, I was curious as to how the Angel could have experienced it without becoming lost in it as well. I was informed that because the Angel was a direct manifestation of God, that it was able to maintain a complete link with God during my entire experience. I had literally been enveloped in the Light of God.

During this last bit of information exchange, the Angel had moved me to yet another level of vibratory existence. This place was more on line with "heavenly" thoughts. I found myself in a place that I can only describe as Grecian in atmosphere. If it had existed on earth, I could have used the term concrete pool and patio, because that was what I first saw. Only, once again, the pool, patio, and entire area was formed from folded light. There were tall white pillars complete with engraved decorative arches. Green ferns and palm trees surrounded the pool area. There were gravel-like pathways that led off from the pool to glorious flower gardens, with white benches for contemplative resting. The water in the pool was clear and blue. Soft blue and green lights seemed to permeate the surrounding atmosphere. I was surprised to see several other "people" wading in various depths of the blue water. I looked at the Angel with question.

"This is a healing area," came the response and I then understood that the "people" who were in the pool were others somewhat like myself. These were people who had a physical body on the earth and who were visiting this place for the healing energies.

"Are those people like me?" I asked, "Are they out of their bodies too?"

"They are here without their physical bodies, yes," came the answer, "but they will remember it more as a dream rather than an actuality."

"And will they be able to receive physical healing from visiting here?"

"Yes," was the answer, "The physical body and "other" bodies that you have are all closely interconnected. What you experience on one level will have an effect on all levels." I was then encouraged to go into the pool; being informed that though I suffered no real ill effects from the densest energy point, I might feel refreshed if I enjoyed the healing waters.

I had no hesitation; the water was beautifully inviting. There were several oval, curved steps that led down into the water and I used them to enter into the pool. "Ahhhhhhhhhhhhhhhh!" I sighed blissfully. It was perfection. I sent my physical body a mental note. "You're going to feel great in the morning!"

I was a little curious about a couple of things, so I took this "time" to question the Angel. Please, never forget that this Angel and I NEVER had ANY of these "conversations," but this is the only way to convey to you our informational exchanges.

"Since everything exists within this vibratory universe," I asked, "in what place or level does the Earth exist?"

"First, know that to use the term "level" is not technically correct, because there are no actual lower or higher levels. There IS vibration, and it is more correct to think in terms of slower or faster vibration, or denser as opposed to more refined or "lighter" energies," the Angel explained.

I then saw a clear mental picture as if looking at a graph paper, with a line stretching from one point on the left and continuing to a point on the far right. The first point on the left would be the densest point that I had just recently experienced and the point on the right would the most refined or fastest vibration point, which I had yet to experience. As I was looking at the graph, another point appeared on it and I knew this to be the vibratory point of the earth. It was located just a little below the midway point.

I was also curious about "hell." The densest point I had experienced was not my definition of the place I had heard so much about while growing up. "Does hell really exist?" I wanted to know.

Yet again, I received one of those yes and no answers. The real nitty gritty answer is that there is ONLY vibration and that everything we experience is something we have created out of, or from that energy. The place I was "visiting" at this moment, for instance, "looked" the way it did for my benefit and understanding only. Therefore, the "fiery, brim-stone Hell where one could burn for eternity" was real...or not, depending on the individual. I received the understanding that no one on Earth could send anyone else living on Earth to "Hell," and that no one had the ability to judge just who would end up there. Very likely, those people who stood in judgement of others, declaring, "You are going to Hell!" would be the very ones to get to experience the vision they so believed in. Other people who might experience that vibration would be people who really believed they belonged there, but because there were many angelic helpers on this side, it didn't usually take long to "get them out of Hell." In other words, Hell is a place created by mankind.

Because I was apparently fascinated with this subject, the Angel decided to show me an example of one self-made creation of hell. The Grecian atmosphere disappeared with the now familiar sensation of movement. I now found myself in what looked to be a dingy, smoky bar, located somewhere on the physical realm of Earth. It was the middle of the night, but very few lights were burning in the bar, so the shadows were long and it was difficult to see. Cigarette smoke hung in the air, adding its pollution to a place that could only be described as a dive. There were only three people there. One of them was a bartender who was cleaning and wiping glasses and two other men who were sitting at a brown wooden bar. One of the two men drinking held a glass of brown liquor in his right hand; his left hand was propping up his chin. The other poor soul was slumped over the bar snoring.

Understand, I am not saying that the bar was a place of hell. In this case, hell was the situation. In addition to the three men who had live physical bodies there was a fourth man there who had "died" not too long ago. This man, who no longer had his physical body, was in "hell." The hell aspect of this situation was that the fourth man had been an alcoholic when he had been alive. He had carried his alcoholism with him when he had passed over and was now unsuccessfully attempting to satisfy his unbearable need for an alcoholic drink. Hell, for him, was his lack of success and the gut-wrenching pain he believed he was experiencing caused by his physical addiction. I watched as this "man in hell" attempted again and again to snatch the glass of liquor from the man who was holding the glass.

Compared to the people and the soul in the bar, the Angel and I shined like bright, blaring, beacons of light. I wondered how in the world the people couldn't see us? We should have been MORE than obvious to eyesight. The Angel picked up my thoughts and answered me. "It's the density of the energies of this "place," and with each individual," it explained. "They cannot see beyond their dense visabilites. This is why it is difficult for helpers to reach these people. Help is standing by, ready to assist, but nothing can be done until the individual realizes he does need help and asks for it. The moment a person opens him or herself to us, you can trust that the opportunity to help is taken advantage of."

I then continued to watch the scene before me develop, as the man who had been holding his glass tilted his head back, opened his mouth and tossed the rest of his drink down his throat. He wiped his mouth with the sleeve of his jacket, then attempted to stand and walk. He managed three staggering steps, then pitched forward to the floor, passing out in an alcoholic stupor. Immediately, the soul without a physical body, threw himself onto the fallen man and tried to lay himself in the other man's physical body!

"Is he trying to possess that other man?!" I asked in astonishment.

"No," came the answer, "he is only attempting feel the alcoholic effects *through* the other man's body. He will not be anymore successful this way than he was before."

"What about the man lying on the floor?" I asked, "Can he be harmed from the other guy lying down in his body like that?"

"No," the Angel replied, "not anymore than the way he has already harmed himself by his sustained habits." The Angel then gave me one last bit of information before transferring me back to the water of the healing pool. "It would be good to remember that any addictions that you have in the physical, you carry with you when you leave."

Once I was standing in the blue waters, the Angel questioned, "Do you want to know of another hell?" Then it answered without waiting for my response. "Real, gut wrenching hell is when you stand enlightened before the Light of Christ and get to experience all the pain and suffering you caused others while on Earth."

I felt uncomfortable. "I've heard of that. I've seen documentaries on television about people who have had near-death experiences and they have what is called a life review." My uneasiness was about my own life. "Am I going to experience a life review as part of this...er...?" (I didn't know what to call these last two nights.)

"You will not be receiving a life review at this time in your life, as it is not necessary for your spiritual development. If it helps you, you could refer to this time as a spontaneous spiritual awakening, although you have not been deficit in your spirituality so far." The Angel clarified that while living my life on Earth I had managed to maintain the minimum degree of spiritual vibration needed in order to make this event possible. "Some choices, some attitudes could have been better, but overall you maintained your spirituality," it informed me. It also informed me that the results of these "experiences" I was having would change me, more than likely giving me a spiritual boost, so to speak; but also as a result, I would be held more responsible for my future choices, because of my new awareness of Spirituality. I knew I would have a lot of thinking to do once this week was over!

I had one more thing I wanted to know, so I asked, "Do you have a name?"

"Do you wish to give me a gender as well?"

Humor! This was the first expression of humor that I had received from the Angel since our first contact when I was screaming about being dead. I was flooded with information. No, the Angel did not have a name. It had its own singular vibration, however, which technically could be called its name, if it were at all translatable into human speech. First, and foremost, Angels are a direct manifestation of God...Conscious Light Beings.   My perception of the Angel had been fairly accurate because I had no real prior conceptions of what one should look like. If I had been locked into the image of a man or woman with wings, my first vision of the Angel might have very well been that. That I was barely able to perceive a human form at all, showed to that specific degree how my thoughts were tainted by my beliefs.

Angels have no will of their own, because they ARE the will of God in action. How they appear to each individual will vary according to the beliefs and expectations of the individual. They will appear in the most comforting, least frightening form possible. How this is made possible, is by the densification of their light-energy. The more the light is densified, the more humanistic they will look and act. Of themselves, they have no personality except what they take on for our benefit. They can take on humor; one could appear to be a stand-up comedian if that is what is needed; but the point is, any personality trait that is attributed them is a temporary aspect for the person with whom they come in contact. Once the task given is fully completed, the Angel is then drawn back into God. An Angel's task could be a brief flicker in time, or take an entire age or two if needed.

After the informational exchanges were complete and I had enjoyed the blue waters of the pool to my satisfaction, the Angel asked me if I was ready to experience Heaven, or in this case, the opposite of what I first experienced.

"So, I will be experiencing the fastest or most refined energies?" I tried to clarify and the Angel affirmed that this would be so.

"Okay then, " I said, "I'm ready," and this is what I experienced:

And this:

Do you think I did that to be funny? Not at all. What I experienced has no words for it. And a good thing too, because using words is going to belittle IT. The truth is, even though I am going to, it would be better not to try. What I experienced cannot be accurately described. I will make the attempt because that is what is expected of me, but though I will put down words and do my best to tell you, you will never really know until you experience it for yourself, because the words I use will not be what happened. So, understand that though the very next words I use will be to tell you, "This is what happened;" it is NOT.

What can I say except that I lost my density? That, in and of itself, is fairly accurate. I became myself to the purest degree of vibration. Let's take it back to the point that I was at the healing pool with the Angel. I communicated to it that I was ready. Then I felt movement within myself. I felt myself expanding; very smoothly stretching out, as if growing circularly outward. I still maintained a center point that I recognized as uniquely myself, and yet as I expanded, I became more and more than just who I have always identified myself as being. I was still Susan, but more.

It was kind of like I became a grid of energy, or a membrane of light that stretched throughout the entire universe. I repeat: the ENTIRE UNIVERSE. To give you just a hint of the magnitude of which I am speaking, let's just say that the entire universe that we are already aware of is but a tiny atomical speck to what really IS.

Now, within this expanded consciousness of me, still being I, I became aware. I knew everything that was happening, everywhere; all at once, simultaneously and separately. I knew and understood the workings of the universe and within the universe the worlds that it contains. I heard the music of the spheres. I saw and understood the mathematics that made the world as we know it. There was not one confusing thing about any of it. I saw and understood the perfection of ALL THERE IS and knew that everything is just as it should be. I was granted the privilege of experiencing total knowledge.

Did I retain any of that knowledge? Nope; hardly a smidgen. Did I want to keep that knowledge? You bet I did! As I was experiencing this wonderful place of Being, at some point I began to feel a contraction of the energy that I am; a pulling in, a movement towards density once again. As that movement was happening and I realized that I was moving "downwards" towards my original self, I could FEEL the knowledge leaving me.

I resisted. I tried to hold on to the complete knowledge that had briefly been mine to know, but could not. It was no longer there. How frustrating to have a memory of an experience that I cannot fully recall! For instance, the mathematical make up of the universe! I can still recall "seeing" the layout of the mathematical numbers, being able to fully comprehend and understand what they meant, but now, though I still have the memory of the visualization, there is no meaning; no understanding; only the memory that I did experience it! While the loss was occurring, I mentally cried out, "No! No! The knowledge is leaving! You want me to teach don't you? Think what a teacher I could be if I could retain this knowledge! How can I teach anything if I'm not able to remember?"

The answer was immediate. "Since everything is vibration, then you must understand that the knowledge you experienced is vibration as well; a very fast, refined energy. The physical body is vibrating energy as well, only it is very dense, slowly moving energy. You can only retain what your physical body will hold. If, while in your physical body, you were to experience the knowledge you just did, your physical body would explode; it would be no more." The Angel then informed me that the night's lessons were over.

At this point, I was beyond caring about my physical body. I no longer had any interest in it whatsoever. It could have laid there in the Valley View and rotted for all I cared. I did not want to go back into it. I wanted to stay on the Heaven side and I communicated this to the Angel in no uncertain terms. I must humbly admit that I cried and carried on almost as badly about having to get back into my body as I did originally when first removed.

The Angel was firm. "You must go back. You were born in order to write this book. It is your karmic fulfillment." And then, though I completely and totally resisted, I was put back into my body.

CHAPTER SIX

Oh, man! I thought I was going to feel good? I felt like I had been body slammed onto a concrete block! Then I realized my body WAS the concrete block. If I can accurately estimate the amount of time it felt like I had been away, I would say I had been away from my body for about 10 years. It felt completely alien to me and in particular, it felt extremely heavy and clumsy! I struggled to sit up in bed, because the blood in my arms had drained down, resulting in temporary numbness and uselessness. I leaned over and squinted to see the time in the darkness. Only 12:30! Just a little more than an hour and a half had passed. It just didn't seem possible that so little time had gone by. The circulation started going in my arms again and I had to endure the excruciating fiery, crawling, tingling sensation, as movement became possible. I stood up and walked around the motel room as I alternately flapped, clapped and rubbed my arms until a semblance of normalcy returned. As I walked in circles I debated if I should sit down and start writing. I knew it was going to take me a while to get the events down and waiting to write would mean that my memory would lose more details than I wanted; but the truth was, I was mentally exhausted and I really wanted to get some UNeventful sleep. That is what I did too. I lay back down, rolled over to my sides with my arms tucked closely to my body and fell into a deep, restful sleep.

I was relatively late in waking, as it was going on 9 AM and I very seldom sleep past 6:30. I rose, stretched, and took a long hot shower. As the steamy water sprayed on and around me, I attempted to reflect on the previous night's events. I still actually felt as numb in my brain as my arms had been. I figured the best thing to do would be to go on to breakfast and just write the events by rote and not try to analyze or make meaning of what I experienced until a later date. With all that I experienced, I wondered if I could ever live long enough to process all that was happening to me?

There was one thing I did wonder about though. One of the last things the Angel communicated to me before forcing me back into my body was that my experiences with it being my teacher were over for now. I had "asked" if I would ever see it again and had received an affirmative reply...only not a date. I didn't get the feeling that it would be any time soon though and I felt saddened by that.

Once I was out of the shower and dressing, I did notice that my blackberry bush scratches were healing at what seemed to be a very remarkable rate. There was no longer any redness of any kind and I could see I would have no scars. As a matter of fact, they were almost completely gone! Despite my mental incapacity, I physically felt in excellent shape. I gathered an extra set of clothes, then left for Ham's.

By this time, all the waitresses knew me by name and I was greeted as an old friend. I was told to pick the table of my choice and a cup of coffee was in front of me before I could slide into the booth. I thanked the waitress, gave my order and immediately began writing as many details as I could remember, searching for words.

Being a regular customer and putting down good tips has its pay offs and I benefited from my generosity by being allowed to sit at breakfast for over two hours. I could tell I had acquired a totally different attitude towards the material I was putting down, because now, when the waitresses inquired about my "novel," I could smile easily, nod my head and agree, yes, I AM in the process of writing a book. About what? Oh, this person goes up on a mountain and meets an angel. "Oh...." they each said. I guess they were hoping for a murder mystery.

When I had gotten down the minimum of a general outline, I stopped writing and left for the Boone Fork Trail. I arrived at the small parking area for Boone Fork just after 1:30. I saw Janet's car there, so I hurried down the path to where the Boone Trail started. Instead of going left down that trail, I turned right, heading again for the Tanawha Trail. Another 200 feet brought me to a bridge that spans Boone Creek. I crossed the bridge then turned and went down the slope to the creek. I looked left and right, but did not see Janet anywhere. I knew she had to be around somewhere and with the sonar I was aware she possessed, I wasn't worried about us finding each other.

I decided to go up the stream. I had never been this way before, so I was looking forward to fresh mountain scenery. I was not disappointed. In Blowing Rock, situated at a lower elevation, the Rhododendrons were in full bloom. Here at 3905 feet, just a slight difference in elevation, the Rhododendrons were budding, but not blooming. Here there was still a profusion of white and pink mountain laurel, so much in fact, along both sides of the creek, it almost looked like clumps of snow on the trees. After my encounter with "Beautiful Bearded Iris," I was anticipating an encounter with an Earthly flower. I wanted to see if I could detect the differences between a biological one grown from the Earth and one created from light. There were no bearded irises blooming here, but there was plenty of mountain laurel. I walked over to a tall bush and leaned in close to a cluster of white

113

blossoms. In all the years I have been visiting the North Carolina Mountains, I had never, up to this point, really looked closely at the flowers that grow here. Looking at the mountain laurel, (I had noticed the same thing about Rhododendrons) I saw that they grow in clusters, as if presenting an entire bouquet at once. Rhododendron blossoms look very similar to azaleas, a Southern flower. Mountain laurel, although it has the characteristic of the bouquet, I found to be very unique. I was intrigued with the tight formulation of the buds and how the bud appears to be pushed open by the flower pistons, rather than unfolding. There are prong-like protrusions on the undersides of the flowers that I also find unusual. I have no botany background whatsoever except the single class I took as a freshman in college, so I have no technical names for anything I am describing. I only know that during my experience with "Beautiful Purple Iris" I had suddenly developed a strong love for all plant life, in particular with flowers of any kind, and right now, at this very moment, I was in love with this individual mountain laurel cluster. I wanted to see if I could detect its Light. I placed my face and eyes to within an inch of the waxy-looking blossoms. I could see some shining glimmers, but maybe that was just a reflection from its "skin." I longed for the elevated conscious state of being I had been in the night before so I could experience this flower as fully as I had "Beautiful Purple Iris." I was not in that state, however, so this cluster and I would remain separate. I knew from the knowledge that I had gained that this flower WAS made from light; only in a much more condensed state. I wondered if this flower was as vividly aware of being alive as had been the Iris? Interesting; I knew the answer to that. The answer was yes. I reached out and gently touched a single blossom from the cluster.

"Thank you for sharing your beauty with me," I whispered to it.

"You could kiss it," a voice called, " but I think the odds on a long distance relationship are against you."

I looked up stream and saw Janet sunning on a flat rock about 100 feet away. "Hi Soliiiiiiiiiiik!" Her name ended with a shriek as I entered into the icy water and started wading up the creek towards her. I would have guessed that back at my house in Charlotte, North Carolina, the temperature was probably 90 degrees. In Blowing Rock, I estimated about 80. Here in the shady creek area with the running, frigid water, the temperature was probably hovering at about 75 and the water was around 40 degrees. My feet quickly numbed and I slowly made my way over to the large flat rock where Janet was sitting.

"Soliiiiiiiiik! That has a nice ring to it." She said grinning at me as I approached. "You think I ought to change my name?"

"I think you're going to have a very sorry life review if you don't stop teasing people so much," I responded.

"Life review? Did you have a life review?" She asked as I climb onto the rock to sit beside her.

I shook my head negatively as I shrugged off my pack and lay it down. "No, couldn't call it that."

"H'mmm..." she said, looking at me with assessment. "How do you feel? Are you able to talk about it yet?"

I shook my ahead again. "I can't even think about it, much less talk about it. My feet are numb right now, but that's nothing compared to my state of mind!"

"Okay, in that case, are you ready to hike up this creek?"

"That, I can handle," I said, getting back to my feet, "I'll just numb my entire body and won't be able to feel anything at all!"

"Yeah! We'll be the walking numbies!"

I turned my head to look at her and she continued, "You know, like an Egyptian mummy? Except we will be the numbies!"

I groaned loudly. "If you are any indication of the humor of God, the world is in serious trouble."

"Too late," she quipped back. "The world is already in trouble."

"Okay, then," I said, preparing to leap into the creek. "Let me help you in your process of numbification!" I did a fanny-spank into the creek, sending up volumes of the cold mountain water all over her.

And I had thought I was a loud screamer! The shrill sound that erupted from her mouth made my ears ring. She was after me in a flash and we began a game of chase up the mountain creek as we splashed, laughed and climbed. It was exactly what I needed.

I would have to describe this particular creek hike as one of the best times of my life. For one reason, it's hard for me to imagine a more beautiful spot on the Earth. When one uses the word beautiful, you have to take in account that person's definition of 'beautiful.' What is their reference point? For me, that definition involves the word green and lots of it.

As I was enjoying all this "green," I reflected on a time when I was touring Egypt. I always had a fascination with the pyramids from way back as a child. I believe I wrote two or three reports on Egypt for school projects growing up. I found the history of the ancient Egyptians completely absorbing as a youth. So, as an adult, when I received the opportunity to go on a group tour to Egypt, I took it. The pyramids and the museum in Cairo proved to be everything I had hoped they would be, but I soon found myself longing for the greenery of the mountains. There was nothing green in Egypt, except for a 50-yard swash of palm trees and brush directly beside the Nile River.

I will never forget a conversation I had with a woman I was seated next to on a tour bus as we were leaving Cairo and going to some other location. We had to drive on a highway that took us right through the Sahara desert. The woman I was seated next to, and myself, were looking out the window of the old, dilapidated bus, staring out at the vast desert before us.

It was the ugliest sight I had ever seen. It was completely devoid of life. There was nothing out there, not even a cactus. Oh, except of course, for the scorpions that lived on God knew what. It was all just sand and rock.

Next to me, seated by the window, Sarah sighed deeply. "Isn't it beautiful?"

I know I looked at her as if she had lost her mind. "You've got to be kidding me," I said. "You find that total wasteland beautiful?"

"You mean you don't?"

I was still staring at her, trying to determine if her brain was in gear. "Uh...no ma'am, I do not find that desert beautiful. I don't find anything beautiful about it at all."

That statement made Sarah very upset. I now figured out that Sarah was one of those people that believe that old malarkey that EVERYTHING is beautiful. Given a plate full of poop, she would find something about it that was beautiful. She was talking to the wrong person. At that time in my life I was still an active police officer and detective and listening to her prattle on and on about what she found beautiful regarding that vast sand box made me want to shock her.

"You find something beautiful in everything don't you?" I asked. She nodded and I continued. "If I describe something to you that I have seen, would you tell me, if you can, what is beautiful about it?"

"Why yes, I would be happy to do that for you!" She smiled and nodded; the teacher of happiness and beauty to all things.

"I am a police officer and the scene I am about to describe to you is in the past, but was very real. I witnessed this scene myself. Are you ready?"

Oh yes, she was ready; she was bouncing up and down in her seat in anticipation of bestowing her wisdom.

I began. "Imagine in your mind's eye an ordinary three bedroom brick house of about 1300 square feet. Someone opens the front door and lets you in and you are instantly hit with the putrefying mixed smell of human excrement, urine and decayed flesh." Her face didn't look so happy now, but I continued. "You are led through the den and down a hallway to a bedroom at the very back of the house. The horrid, putrid smell increases with every step until you have to start breathing through your mouth in an attempt to lessen the effects of the odor. When you step into the room you see the cause of the smell. On the right side of the door is a bed with a dead man laying on it. He has been dead for several days and his body has started to decompose. Still lying in his mouth is a Colt .357 Magnum that he used to blow out the back of his head. The pillow is brown now, covered in dried blood and brain tissue. Pieces of bone and brain are splattered over the headboard and the wall behind him. He stinks; not only from the decaying tissues, but because when he died, his bladder and his bowels let go. Now Sarah, can you tell me ANY thing beautiful about that?"

It was probably the cruelest act I had ever deliberately committed. Sarah sat beside me now, tears streaming down her face, sobbing unashamedly. She opened her eyes and insisted. "The desert is beautiful, it is!"

"I know you have this deep desire to convince me that this desert is beautiful, but Sarah, my definition of beauty is not the same as yours. Are you talking about the power of the desert?" I asked. "Are you saying that the power of the desert is what makes it beautiful?"

"Yes!" she agreed. "The power of the desert is what makes it beautiful!"

I thought for a moment. "Yes, I agree with you that the desert is powerful. It is one of the most powerful scenes of nature I have ever seen. Its power is the authority of death. It can kill you easily, with no thought or remorse. But the fact that is it is powerful, does not also make it beautiful to me."

She looked ready to protest, but I continued. "You have to understand my definition of beauty. This desert, in my mind, is the antithesis of beauty. To me, beautiful is green, beautiful is life; and this desert is devoid of all that I consider beautiful."

"It is beautiful! It is!" she insisted.

"Sarah, give it up. There is nothing you can say that will convince me this pile of sand is beautiful." Shortly thereafter, she moved to another seat.

Here, now, in this mountain creek, was what I consider the ultimate of Earthly beauty. Short of heaven, which I had now experienced, there was nothing I knew of on Earth that could be more appealing. Abundant greenery surrounded me on both sides and above. The water, though admittedly freezing cold, was crystal clear as it moved swiftly down the mountain. Series of miniature waterfalls appeared every 10 feet or so, falling from heights of two and three feet. More than a hundred different species of birds flew around and twittered merrily. Squirrels chattered and played chase with one another imitating us in the creek. Though I couldn't see them, I was aware of the abundant wildlife surrounding me, including deer, raccoons, ground hogs and foxes. I knew there were bears in the hills as well, but knew them to be shy creatures, usually only showing themselves early in the morning or at night. My point in all this is that there is no place on Earth I know of that is so refreshingly alive and more beautiful than these North Carolina Mountains. It might not quite be heaven, but it's as close as you can get.

All of that, just to tell you why I was enjoying myself so much! But it was more than just the scenery around me; it was the company I was keeping as well. After the mind-blowing sessions I had so recently experienced, there was no one I knew of whom I could have felt more comfortable around than Janet. Neither my husband, Jerry, nor my daughter, or anyone else I had ever known would have been able to easily comprehend or accept what I would have told them about the past few days; no one except this new found friend, Janet/Solomon.

During our trek up the stream we came to a place where the creek widened to approximately 30 feet. There was a two-foot wide, three-foot drop waterfall into this area that formed a pool with the deepest depth of around six feet. It was over my head, so that was plenty deep! There was another broad, flat rock that was positioned just over the pool and it made a good sitting or jumping off point next to the water. By the time we reached this area, we certainly qualified as real "numbies," so we climbed out of the water and sat, shivering in the sunlight that filtered through the tree tops, until we could get sufficiently warm again.

By this time, I felt like I was ready to talk about the previous night's experience, but when we sat down on the smooth rock, Janet looked at me and said, "Well, Grace, are you ready to have a philosophical discussion about God now?"

I was consumed by raw emotion. My throat closed up and my eyes welled over with tears. I opened my mouth, but nothing came out. I silently shook my head and instead reached into the back pack I still managed to bring up the creek, then handed her my journal to read.

She took it and asked, "Can I read all you've written so far?"

I shrugged. I didn't care. So, she started reading and I zoned out by listening to all the different sounds of the rushing waters while she read my personal recordings. It took her about an hour and a half to read my notes. "Not bad, Grace, not bad," she said handing the journal back to me when she had finished.

"What do you think?" I automatically asked as I put it back.

"Graaaaaaaace..." she drew the word out in a plaintive wail. "What I think is that you're a better writer than you are a talker."

"Well, DUH!" I responded. "I have such a bad case of foot in mouth disease that most often, I don't stick one foot into my mouth, I stuff both of them in! But that's not a surprise to you is it?"

"Seeing as how all I get is a sound like a gargle when I ask you a question, it's no surprise at all. But seriously, Susan, it's a good outline so far."

"So far? The Angel told me its visits with me were done."

"That may be, but there is still something missing in here."

"Oh, Solomon," I playfully questioned with sarcasm, "Oh wise angel from above, what is it?"

Water hit me in the face. "Smart Ass. And you think I'm going to have a sorry life review?" We both laughed, then she continued. "Okay, just because you're not going to see the Angel for a while is beside the point. The last section where you experienced the fastest vibration? I believe you've left out some information."

I sputtered, my tongue tangled into knots. "Out? Out?!" I finally exclaimed. "You think I don't know what I've left out? Why I didn't put anything in! I didn't say anything about God! You want to try?" I asked, searching around inside my backpack for my pen. "You think you can do better? I want you to try! I want you to do better than I've done." I found my pen, grabbed one of her hands and slapped my blue-inked Gel-writer into her palm. "Seriously! Give it a try and see if you can put THAT into words!"

There was a period of silence, as Janet looked down at the pen in her hands and twirled it round and round in quiet contemplation. I, on the other hand, was pacing circles of furious frustration. After a moment or two, Janet stood up and looked at me solemnly, holding her chin in her left hand as she regarded me. "Susan..."

"What?!" I snapped, stopping in front of her.

She laid a hand on my right arm, looking directly into my eyes. "Are you okay?"

I could see the concern she was feeling for me in her eyes. I knew that she had not meant to offend me. I felt some of the anger I was feeling dissipate; though the frustration at my inability to accurately express what I had experienced remained. I took a deep breath and tried to relax. "I'm okay, " I said in a reluctant way.

"Good, Susan, that's good," she responded, then put her other hand on my left arm. "Now let me tell you what I want you to do." She shoved me backwards as hard as she could into the creek. "CHILL OUT!" she shouted, as I hit the six-foot deep pool and went under.

You want to talk about shock therapy? I had been sitting in the sun for over an hour and a half and had completely dried and warmed up. When I hit that icy mountain water, it felt so cold, it burned my skin like a raging fire. The scream that involuntarily left me came out while I was still under the water, and the gasp for air was just as reflexive. I shot up out of the water gasping and coughing with a complete attitude adjustment having been made. Janet was smirking at me as I climbed back out. "I always knew you were going to shove me off the side of a mountain," I grunted as I sat back down beside her.

Her clear, hearty laugh rang out and she reached over and gave me a hard squeezing hug. "Oh, Grace, Grace! When I said something was missing, I wasn't being critical, you know! All I was trying to tell you is that I don't believe that you're finished having your experiences."

"Really?" I asked. "Why do you say that?"

She turned around on the flat rock where we were sitting so that we would be facing each other. She sat cross-legged, staring at me intently for a moment as she gathered her thoughts. "What the angel told you is

123

accurate, you know," she began, speaking slowly and deliberately, "when you were experiencing the fastest or most refined vibration, you experienced much more than you were able to put down or even remember."

"Yes, yes, I know," I said, breaking in. "That's why I got so frustrated earlier. It's maddening to me that I'm not able to remember everything! It's like, well, what's the purpose then? What good is there to experience something if you can't tell it, or even worse, not remember all of it? Why have even bothered to share all this with me?"

"But you see, it hasn't been lost," she contradicted. "Everything you experienced is still there...you just have to be able to access it."

"Access it? You mean like accessing information on a computer?"

"Sort of," she agreed, speaking even more slowly, "but the way you access it is by raising your physical energies, so that you can hold those higher energies. The more you are able to raise your physical vibrations, the more you will be able to remember."

"Oh." I said thoughtfully, then shook my head. "How am I going to raise my physical energies if I'm suppose to get this information down in one week?"

She didn't say anything, but looked at me pointedly.

"Oh!" I exclaimed. "That's why you said I was going to have more experiences! I'm going to get my energies raised? But how? Who?" I asked when she continued to be silent.

She pursed her lips and continued just to stare at me. I knew she was receiving information and just wasn't saying what she knew. I grabbed her left arm with my right hand, leaning in.

"Janet, tell me."

"It's not that simple, Susan," she answered. "I've told you before and you yourself know now that the information I get is not put into words, so that leaves room for individual interpretation. And besides, just because I received information, doesn't necessarily mean it's correct for me to tell you. Knowing about something happening in advance can very often be the catalyst to stop the event from happening."

"Can you tell me anything?" I asked, again starting to feel familiar anxiety.

There was silence as she contemplated. After a moment or two she spoke, "Susan, all I can tell you is when I ask, I see The Light."

CHAPTER SEVEN

That evening I had dinner at the "Speckled Trout Café," just two spots down from "Cheeseburgers" on the corner at Main Street. Once again Janet had declined to have a meal with me, telling me like she had before, she had 'things to do.' When I pressed her about those 'things' she laughed at me like she always does and said, "Grace, trust me, some time after this week is over, I'll fill you in on all the boring details of my life. But for right now, it's just better that I go."

The "Speckled Trout"...you know, I just like the sound of that name. It's a quaint little restaurant; established since 1986. That's what the little blue menu says anyway. It's another spot with good food and reasonable prices. This night I decided not to have a regular meal, but ordered several things from the list of appetizers. I tried the smoked trout, the stuffed mushrooms and the escargot. I've never understood exactly why I like to eat snails, but I really do like them and they are a specialty at this restaurant. I decided that I could manage a single glass of Chardonnay, followed by iced water and lemon.

After my meal I strolled down Main Street, looking into all the windows of the quaint looking shops as I passed. I walked on by the park where tourists sat on the many benches lining the street and where children were still playing on all the available playground equipment. When I came to "Kilwin's Chocolates," I went inside. M'mmmm, "Kilwin's" doesn't just make chocolates; they make a variety of chocolate candy, different types of homemade fudge, and some of the most delicious homemade ice cream a person could ever hope to have.

They also make their very own cones. You can get a regular, ordinary type; you know the one that has the texture and taste of a piece of cardboard paper, or you can get a homemade, chocolate coated cone; or a sugar coated cone. There is a whole list of just the different kinds of cones you can get to go with the ice cream!

Obviously, I am into the ice cream. Now, there is Rocky-Road and Praline Cream and well, you name it, they have it. However, I am a plain chocolate ice cream lover, and as a matter of fact, my preferred cone is the one that looks and tastes like cardboard paper; so that's what I bought.

The entire time that I ate, strolled and consumed my ice cream, I was doing what Janet told me not to do: thinking. After she had made her comment about "The Light," we had gone back down the creek to where we had started and very politely turned our backs to each other, changing into dry clothes. After that was when I had invited her to dinner and she had declined. I was thinking all right, because the phrase "The Light" was stuck in my head. Janet knew it would be, because the last thing she said to me as she drove out of the parking lot at Boone Creek was, "Try not to think about it!"

I'm quite sure that anyone who knows the least bit about psychology knows that the more one tries not to think about something, the more a person does!

The Light, the Light, the Light, over and over again, round and round in my head. Where could I find information about the Light? A thought occurred to me. The Bible. There was probably information in The Bible. Where could I find a Bible though? Then I knew. I hurriedly finished my ice-cream cone and hastened back to my car and then to the Valley View. I walked into my room and straight to the small table set between the two double beds. The table had a single drawer. I opened it. Inside, as I knew there would be, was a Gideon Bible. I picked it up, then sat on the edge of my bed and started thumbing through it. It's hard to admit, having been the child of a United Methodist Minister, that I wasn't as familiar with the Bible as I should be. I had a distant memory of some phrase like, "In the beginning was the Word," and I had a vague memory that it mentioned the Light, but I couldn't remember from where it came. I was thinking that The Light must have been referring to The Christ, so I started with the New Testament. Matthew? No. Mark? No. Luke? No. John? Ah! I found it!

The Gospel According to Saint John, Chapter 1. "In the beginning was the Word, and the Word was with God, and the Word *was* God." Wowwwwww, I thought. What else could it be referring to but vibration! The spoken word is the result of the vibration of the vocal cords, emitting sound, which is also vibration. From my recent experiences, I had been told over and over and over that everything was vibration and this verse in The Bible was verifying that for me.

I read further: verse 2, verse 3, then verse 4, "In him was life; and the life was the light of men." The Light of men...okay, now I was getting to something here. I started reading aloud the following verses. "And the Light shineth in darkness; and the darkness comprehended it not. There was a man sent from God, whose name was John. The same came for a witness, to bear witness of the Light, that all men through him might believe. He was not that Light, but *was sent* to bear witness of that Light. *That* was the true Light, which lighteth every man that cometh into the world. He was in the world, and the world was made by him and the world knew him not. He came unto his own, and his own received him not. But as many as received him, to them gave he power to become the sons of God, even to them that believe on his name: Which were born, not of blood, nor of the will of the flesh, nor of the will of man, but of God. And the Word was made flesh, and dwelt among us, (and we beheld his glory, the glory as of the only begotten of the Father,) full of grace and truth."

I pondered over these words for a while, trying to make sense of them. It seemed pretty obvious it was saying that first, The Word, (or the vibration) was God and that The Light came from The Word and was also The Word, so was also God as well as being the child of God. The Light, being The Christ, became flesh, or Jesus. Apparently then, as now, God had called for volunteers to be born, who would then assist in the undertaking that had been called for, and John the Baptist was one of those volunteers. More than likely all those men and women who had followed; the disciples and the prominent women of His life had also volunteered beforehand to give assistance in this great endeavor to touch and teach mankind.

So what did all of this have to do with me? I had been told I was one of the many volunteers. Was I being called upon to be a witness of The Light? The thought made me extremely uncomfortable. Why in the world would I be chosen for something of that magnitude? I was not prominent by anyone's standards. In my life I had been a social worker, a police officer and was currently a manager of an educational testing company. It was inconceivable that anyone was going to consider me a valid authority on anything to do with God. I took a deep breath and sighed loudly. One thing was for sure, I was not relaxed about the night before me.

I closed the Bible, then went outside onto the cement porch, again sitting in one of the old plastic rockers. I began rocking slowly back and forth as I fixed my eyes to the heavens above me, continuing to ponder on all that had happened to me over the course of the past few days and wondering what was before me. I had both of my hands resting on the rocking chair arms, and happened to be looking down at my right hand as I shook my head in perplexity and briefly closed my eyes.

It could have only been for a second, certainly not longer than that. When I reopened my eyes, I was still looking down at my right hand, only it was no longer *MY* hand. It was also no longer resting on the arm of the old, white plastic rocking chair, but laying instead on an even older rough hewn plank of a wooden table. I didn't move a muscle. Immediate animal instinctiveness came to the forefront, or it could have been old police training, but either way, I wanted to make no sudden moves until I could figure out what was happening!

For a moment I just studied the hand resting on the table, noting the differences between what it was and what it *should* be. In size, they were similar; wide palms, long fingers and a long narrow thumb. The hand that I was staring at, however, could not be mine because it was a hand obviously used to hard labor. There was muscularity that mine lacked, along with firm calluses, which my hand also lacks. Nope, definitely not my hand. Then whose hand was it?! Though still unmoving I was feeling a well-known panic. I moved my eyes to the left and right, then quickly focused on the hand again. I was not sitting on the porch at the back of the Valley View anymore. I was somewhere entirely different. WHERE?! I continued to stare at the hand for a moment and just listened. I knew that I was in a room I had never seen before, and from outside, I could hear people talking loudly or laughing, and then the sounds of braying mules, the baaing of sheep and the creaking of carts as they moved by small open windows in the walls.

The sounds only added to my confusion. I moved my eyes from my right hand to look at my left hand, which also was not my hand, which was laying in my lap, which was also not mine. The left hand I viewed was actually resting on the left thigh, separated by cloth of thick-woven, light brown, raw cotton. I lifted my eyes and took a swift look at the room again before staring down at the lap. I was in a small single room, approximately 20 by 20 with no exits except for the one door that led outside. The floor and the walls all seemed to be made of clay bricks, worn from age and leaving fine, pale orange dust on the table and chairs. These were not modern bricks, but hand-made with bits of straw in them and hardly more than mud. There were no decorations adorning the walls, and the door itself could not even be called a door, because the only separation from inside to out was a sheath of frayed dirty, gray cloth, strung on a cord. Beside the long wooden table were matching long wooden benches and chairs. Sitting on the benches and chairs were men who were speaking quietly to each other and, by their manner, appeared to be waiting for something or someone.

Trying to appear nonchalant, I lifted the right hand that was not mine and cupped my chin, which of course, I knew now was not my face. I felt a beard. I don't have a beard! I ran the hand up the face, feeling features foreign to me. I casually soothed the hair, and felt a cascade of shoulder length, waving hair. I took a long slow intake of breath, then slowly expelled, willing myself to be calm. There was a man sitting to the right of me. His skin was

131

swarthy and dark from the sun. His hair was black, long and curling and he had a black curly beard as well. He was dressed in a robe of many colorful stripes. I watched him as he picked up a ripe, pinkish-brown fig from a filled bowl of pottery, then bit the fig in half. As he chewed, he leaned close to me and spoke in a foreign language. I felt shock. I had never heard that language spoken, but I understood what he asked! In his own tongue he had asked, "Jeshua, where is Judas?"

Jeshua! I was in the body of Jesus?! It was an even greater shock as this body then spoke back to the man, answering in the same foreign language, and yet I again understood what was said. Jeshua and I both answered, "Do not be concerned, he will be here soon."

I could not deny it to myself anymore. I was somehow, someway, sitting inside the body of Jesus, having no understanding how it occurred, but realizing I had traveled back 2000 years to exist in this moment in time. I was very aware that the "I" that is Susan was in the body of Jesus and simultaneously aware that the "I" that is Jesus was aware of the "I," Susan. Paradoxically, while each of us was aware of the other, the recognition was that the "I" that was each of us was the same I! As a matter of fact, the "I," Jesus, welcomed me with love and understanding and even expressed some humor at my shock.

Then I blinked.

WHUMP! I was back in my own body, sitting in the white plastic rocker, back at the Valley View. I leapt from the chair as if the chair had electrocuted me and flew to my room on frantic feet. I threw myself onto my bed and screamed into the foam pillow so the people in the room next door wouldn't think I was being murdered. What was going on? I was mind-boggled. How could something like that have happened? What did it mean?! I questioned my sanity. Is it possible that I was just having some severe hallucinations brought on by stress? I was trembling all over from reaction to the event.

I remained on the bed for a long time, clutching the pillow as if it could save my life if need be. Eventually, after a long time passed with nothing more eventful happening, I managed to calm down. After what felt like an hour, I sat up on the bed. It was still early in the evening; just past eleven. I decided to write down what had happened while it was still fresh in my mind. After writing, I felt much calmer, but was still having trouble understanding what that event had been all about. Time-wise, I had existed in that place and Being for less than a full minute, but what I had experienced was just so beyond my belief as being possible! It was so very difficult to understand and accept that the "I" that is Susan and the "I" that is Jesus could be separate and yet the same "I." It was incomprehensible to me. I paced around the small motel room wishing more than anything that I could talk to Janet and wondering why I had never thought to ask her for a telephone number where she could be reached. I glanced at the clock again. Well...I guess calling at 1:30 in the morning would be a bit inappropriate. At 2:00 AM, I finally wound down and felt tired enough that I thought I could go to sleep, so I lay on my chosen bed and made an attempt. Didn't happen. I tried counting sheep and made it to 1054 before I stopped. Then I decided not to try and just lay there and listen to some music. I reached for the clock/radio and went through some stations until I found one playing nighttime love songs. Yeah, easy listening; that's my style.

In the middle of the night there is very little talk on the radio and for that I was glad. I listened to the crooning sounds of Luther Vandross, heard Dan Hill singing "Sometimes When We Touch," and felt myself starting to sink into sleep as I heard Benny Mardones begin singing, "Into The Night." As I was shifting into a more dream-like state, the words of the song changed just slightly to me, and instead of hearing the word night, I heard, "I'll take you into the Light," so that to me the song became something else. I heard:

> "She's just sixteen years old
> Leave her alone they say
> Separated by fools
> Who don't know what love is yet
> But I want you to know...
> If I could fly
> I'd pick you up
> I'd take you into the Light
> And show you a love
> Like you've never seen-ever seen
> It's like having a dream
> Where nobody has a heart
> It's like having it all
> And watching it fall apart
> And I would wait till the end of time
> for you
> And do it again it's true
> I can't measure my love
> There's nothing to compare it to
> But, I want you to know...
> If I could fly
> I'd pick you up
> I'd take you into the Light

> And show you a love
> Like you've never seen-ever seen
> If I could fly
> I'd pick you up
> I'd take you into the Light
> I'd take you into the Light
> Into the Light
> Into the Light
> Into the Light"

I drowsily closed my eyes and smiled to myself. What a nice song. I liked it very much. I was almost asleep, but not quite. Then I noticed that the music had stopped playing. Had the radio gone dead? I started coming back to wakefulness as I listened. Instead of the radio all I could hear were the outside night sounds: crickets, frogs, locusts, ecetera...but...the sounds did seem to be awfully loud...and did I hear water running? My feet were wet!

Wide-awake, I snapped my eyes open. I gasped in open-mouthed shock and terror as I immediately threw my arms out wide in an attempt to throw myself backwards.

Why? Because when I opened by eyes, I was standing in a creek bed at the very lip-edge of a waterfall that had a 400-foot drop! Okay, I said I had conquered most of my fears of heights, but not ALL of them! And when I opened my eyes and found myself just at the point where I could easily fall over...I was filled with fear all over again. I mean my toes were sticking out into thin air!

When I threw my arms out, my right arm struck human flesh. Instinctively, my fingers curled into that body and I grasped hard as I turned to also grab with my left hand. Hell, if I were going to go over, I wouldn't be going over alone! As I turned, I also looked to see who

135

was standing beside me and gasped again; this time in recognition. I was staring into the face of a man whom I knew could only be Jesus.

CHAPTER EIGHT

I felt my knees crumbling beneath me and I grasped onto him harder as I tried desperately to remain standing. "Uh...uh..." I stammered, "Uh, excuse me, heights aren't my favorite thing."

And I thought Janet liked to laugh at me. He not only laughed at me; he belly laughed like I had said the funniest thing he had ever heard. But, even as he laughed, he obligingly turned and put an arm around me, and walked me six or seven feet away from the edge of the cliff. I was still standing in the creek, but at least I was no longer in danger of falling over!

Have you ever had an experience in everyday life that while you are going through it, you outwardly appear calm, but inside your mind is whirling? That was my state of mind as I stood there in that creek bed next to Jesus. It was like, "I'm standing next to Jesus, I'm standing next to Jesus, I'm standing next to Jesus!" When we had walked what I considered a safe distance from the edge of the waterfall, Jesus turned, took me by both my hands and looked deeply into my eyes.

His eyes ARE blue, wide-spaced and large. I could see light shining in them, similarly as I had with "Beautiful Purple Iris." His eyes sparkled with life, intelligence, wisdom and above all, Love.

"Susan...I AM you and you are me. Do you get it?" Oh, the LOVE I felt emanating from him to me! But, I did not have a clue as to what he was talking about, so I hung my head, feeling ashamed and said no. He lifted my chin so I could still see his eyes and answered as he smiled, "You WILL get it." Then, grinning wickedly at me with white, even teeth, he turned and walked back over to the edge of the waterfall, turned his back to the edge and faced me, spreading his arms out wide. "Okay, take a good look! I know you'll want to describe me."

My knees finally gave out and I sank down into the shallow water of the creek, shaking my head dazedly. Was this real? I had certainly never had a dream like this before! Was I out of my physical body? That seemed most likely, although this was different than when the Angel had pulled me out of my body. There was no experience of a separation; I was just suddenly here! The strangest thing to me was the fact that it didn't seem like I was in some heavenly place removed from Earth or some other realm. This had a closeness to physical reality that was confusing. I did have a physical body. I pinched myself. Yes, this was a physical body. Though barefoot, I was still wearing my blue jean shorts and cotton T-shirt. I gave a brief look around me. I knew exactly where I was; I had been here many times. This was Chimney Rock Park, and I was sitting in the creek water at Hickory Nut Falls. This was very interesting seeing as how Chimney Rock is an hour and a half drive south from the motel at Blowing Rock. But, when you compared this with the rest of my week, it wasn't any stranger than anything else I had already been through! What was one more thing to figure out among hundreds?

Jesus was waiting at the edge of the falls. His head was half cocked to one side, looking at me quizzically as if asking, "Are you okay?"

Well, the truth was, no I wasn't, but I was hanging in there the best I could. I suddenly remembered I was supposed to be looking at him so I could describe him; so I concentrated on that, as I tried to get my mind into some semblance of order.

The man standing in front of me looked to be over six feet tall, maybe six-three or six-four. He was wearing the same long, light brown robe of heavy raw cotton that came down to his ankles and was tied with a sash of the same cotton material. He wore brown leather sandals on his feet. Because of the robe, I cannot give an accurate description of his physical body, but from his movements, and from actually touching him, I can tell you that he was quite physically fit. Slim, with hard muscularity. His skin was a dark gold, and his shoulder length hair was a medium auburn brown, heavily streaked with shimmering reds, swept back off a high forehead. His beard was the same color as his hair, and neatly trimmed. All his features were large, his eyes, his nose and mouth. The bridge of his nose was high and straight, the lips long and curving upright. He was....or I should say IS a very handsome man.

"Uh......Jesus?" I asked hesitantly. "Is this the way you looked when you lived on Earth?"

He shrugged his shoulders; "More or less, it's the way I look right now."

"More or less?"

"Yes. Your perceptions of me are colored by your expectations. Remember that you have the same power to create that I do and this experience you are having is a joint one. I would probably look somewhat different to someone else, but this is close." He stopped and looked at me intently for a moment. "Really? So, you want to know what I *really* look like?"

He had read my mind! I felt extreme discomfort over that. This wasn't like the experience I had when I was out of body with the Angel. During that experience my conscious thought had been raised, and the Angel and I had seemed a part of each other. It had been a flow of give and take. Conversation had not really existed. This experience with Jesus felt like it was completely on a physical level, as if I could have just run into him on the street! His consciousness was complete, but I was still just exactly the same old Susan, same old personality. He was right. I did want to see what He looked like in his true form. Before I even had time to think of those sentences above, in front of my eyes a shift occurred. The physical man, Jesus, disappeared; along with a section of Chimney Rock Park and the mountains beyond it. At the edge of the waterfall, just at the point where the drop occurs, a window in space appeared and I looked into the Universe. To the left of me, to the right of me and including the spot where I was sitting was still Chimney Rock Park, but seven feet in front of me was nothing but the Universe. Well, that's actually incorrect; because what was in front of me was nothing but The Christ Light.

How puny to say, It is all there is! I understood that The Christ Light is not separate from God. Nothing was removed from God. The Christ Light is a direct replication of God; an all-enhancing creation, and that The Christ on Earth appearing as Jesus WAS a miracle. There were Christed individuals before Jesus the Christ, Melchizadek and Buddha for example; who were Christ-like but not The Christ. We, as human beings, are of the Earth and from the Earth, with the exception of our spirituality, which is from the Light. Jesus was different. He was a direct creation from that Light.

What I saw before me was Creative Love Consciousness, appearing to me to be a Light of such brilliance that I could see nothing but it before me. It wasn't a light that burned like the sun, I did not have to draw my eyes away for fear of being blinded or because of pain. I can draw upon my original description of the Angel, because this Light was similar to the Angel; a direct manifestation of Light; only the Light in front of me NOW was ALL; everything. I was already sitting down, which was a good thing; because I would have just fallen down again if I had been standing.

Now, I have to tell you I was overcome with a desire to Be with that Light, to become a part of it; so drawn to it, that I got to my knees and then my feet and began a wobbling totter towards it. If I could have, I would have made a running, flying leap at the edge of the waterfall, right into the center of that Light. As it was, however, just when I got to the place where I was about ready to jump, the vista before me disappeared and the man Jesus reappeared, physically stopping me from making a 400-foot fall. He once again assisted me away from the drop-off, this time helping me to climb over the wooden fence that separates hikers from the dangerous edge, then hopped nimbly over himself. Once he was over he stood and looked the place over, then took a deep breath, making a sigh of happiness. "This is a really nice place, don't you think so, Susan?"

"M'ph," I grunted. I wasn't actually capable of speech at this point. I was just hanging onto the fence, concentrating on keeping my knees from buckling.

"Susan, you're clutching that fence there like your legs are still weak. Would you like to sit down?" Jesus asked, coming toward me solicitously and taking me by the elbow. He started leading me to the wooden steps and ramps that were part of the trail. "Here," he said, leading me to a set of steps. "Sit down here." I gratefully sat and then he walked over to another waterfall that is part of the same creek. The drop from above is only about 8 feet and creates a shower like place that hikers stand under on hot summer days. I watched him as he walked to the spot where the water fell in a hard cascade. He put his right hand out and let the water rush over his hand. A moment later, he turned and grinned at me, then stepped underneath the spray, letting the water soak him from head to toe. He spread his arms wide, leaned back and tilted his head, opening his mouth and letting the water rush in as he slowly turned in a circle. Then he shouted, "HA!" The sound came deep from his diaphragm and was a sound of pure joy. Walking out of the shower he began shaking himself vigorously, spraying water all around him. He flung his wet hair off his face as he walked back to me. "Ah, Susan, that was fun!" He said, sitting down next to me on the wooden steps. He picked up my left hand and held it. "Got a question, Susan?"

"Uh, yes," I stammered, clearing my throat. He gave me a moment to gather my poor, scattered thoughts before I began. "Uh, yes," I repeated, "Uh, you know, I... Jesus... I've had a lot of things happen to me the last few days; I've been out of my body, I've seen an angel, I'm seeing YOU!" I picked up speed, rushing ahead in case he might interject with something, but he remained silent as I continued. "What I'm wondering now is... am I really here? Okay, I mean, I know I'm really here, but am I out of my body? Do I have a physical body still waiting for me in the Valley View, or is all of me here?"

There was a pause as Jesus studied my hand in his. He rubbed the back of my hand with his palm, then turned my hand over, running his palm and fingers over my palm. Then he spoke. "Susan, you come from the perspective that your life as Susan living in a physical body is real, whereas from my perspective, your life in the physical is an illusion. So, from your perspective, yes, where we are now is just as real as your so-called everyday existence. If you desire a name for it, some would call what you're experiencing BI-location, or physically being in two places at once. You're not really in two places at once, where we are now is a degree removed from the vibration where you usually are. It still qualifies as a physical reality though. Does that answer your question?"

Say what?! "Uh, I guess so," I answered, stammering again.

"Good!" He responded, hopping up and pulling me with him. He pulled me by the hand to a roughly triangular area that is approximately twenty-five feet square. When we were in the center, he took my other hand as well, then gave me a huge smile. "I want to dance," he announced. "Dance with me, Susan." He started swaying back and forth. "Come on, come on!" He urged, as I was slow to respond. I hesitantly started swaying as well and when I was moving to the rhythm he liked, he dropped my hands and started snapping his fingers and kicking his feet. "Stand beside me and do as I do," he said, so I moved to his left side and tried to move as he did. I don't know what to call the dance we were doing. From my experience as a non-dancer, I would have to call it some sort of line dancing; possibly a Jewish dance of celebration. First we took a step to the right, then kicked with our left foot, and then we stepped to the left and kicked our right foot. We did that several times then turned around in a circle, starting the process over again. We began rather slowly, then picked up speed as we continued. Before long, it felt like I was running in place, and Jesus started moving back and forth away from me, then circling me; humming and snapping his fingers, kicking and clapping; a whirlwind of movement. I managed to keep stepping and kicking as he moved all over the place. I didn't know what I was doing, but I was having a fun time. Jesus kept encouraging me to move, so finally I gave up trying to follow his steps and just moved and kicked and jumped anyway that felt comfortable. I was sure I looked laughable and started laughing at myself. Jesus laughed right along with me. I began improvising and started treating it like a square dance. I grabbed one of his arms and swung around shouting, "Do se do!"

"Do se do!" He shouted right back and we both laughed heartily.

After a while, I realized I was no longer uncomfortable around him and knew that he had asked me to dance for that very purpose. I reached a level of exhaustion and begged to stop, walking over to the cascading waterfall where Jesus had showered earlier. I let the water rush over my head; although icy cold, it felt great! Jesus came over and stood next to me, repeating his actions from before.

"Feeling better now? Not as nervous?" he asked as we both left the spray.

"Yes, I do feel better," I answered, "Thanks, that was fun."

"Yes, I enjoyed that tremendously," he said and then added, "Okay, now that you're feeling more comfortable around me, we can get down to business." He led me back to the wooden steps where I had been sitting earlier and I sat back down looking up at him expectantly.

He surprised me by easing himself on to the stone ground in front of me, sitting with his legs crossed in what I found out later is called a "lotus" position. With his height, we were actually sitting at the same level. "I guess it's pretty accurate to say that you've been overwhelmed by everything you've experienced isn't it?" he asked. I nodded with exaggeration to show my agreement and he continued. "You have also wondered why you were chosen for this." I nodded again. He paused, studying me for a moment before saying, "Let me put it this way. You weren't exactly chosen, you just ended up being the one."

"How is that?" I asked.

"Well, there did have to be some pre-qualifications; some measurements of spiritual awareness and abilities that had to be met and you met those qualifications easily enough. There were some people that were more spiritually oriented than you; some had better intuitive abilities; others had greater mental capacities. There are of course, better writers. One of *your* best qualities is your total lack of malice. It's completely lacking in you. You have respect for and display your care for all individuals. In other words, you display an unconditional love for mankind. We also have to take into account a willingness factor, which you met adequately as well. So, you see, it wasn't that it just had to be you, it just ended up as you. You could have also said no and really meant it, and then it would have been someone else entirely."

"Oh," I responded, not sure I really understood what he was saying, "so, I just sort of lucked into it?"

"Hardly!" he laughed. "No, in this case, luck had nothing to do with it, although there were some factors of opportunity and availability in the mix. You could say that the total combination of who you are led to this."

I remembered something the Angel had said, "The Angel told me I had been born for this."

"Yes, that's true," he answered, "but don't forget that free will always plays a factor in any event."

I nodded my head as if I understood, thinking ahead to another question. Just as I opened my mouth to ask, however, he answered me.

"No, when I said, I am you and you are me, I was not talking about reincarnation. You, Susan, were not Jesus during that time I lived in this physical body. I'll help you with that understanding a little later. Right now I just want to give you some information to pass on to those whom you can reach by writing your story."

I felt some relief on hearing that. I felt egocentric even considering the possibility, but had wanted to ask just to be sure. Jesus leaned over and gently grasped my right forearm. "I want you to pay close attention as I speak. Don't worry about remembering every word. Understand? It's more important that you just hear what

I'm saying. When the time comes for you to put it down in writing, I will help you. For now, just listen."

I nodded yet again and he let go and sat up straight bringing his hands together so that the tips of his thumbs just touched.

"This message is for all the people of the Earth. And the key word here is ALL, for you are all mine. I have charge over each and every one of you. My message to you today is very simple and the most important thing I want you to know is this: **I love you exactly the way you are.** If you understand nothing of what I say after this statement, do know this: I love you exactly the way you are."

I am inserting a description here because there is one thing I have yet to describe about Jesus and that is his voice. I had noticed the quality of it the moment I first heard him speak, but now as he spoke with such clear earnestness, I was struck with it again. I have to shake my head at myself for trying. I am going to put into letters and words something that can only be experienced and understood by sound and hope that you can grasp a little of it. His voice is musical. The first thing you might hear is a clear strong baritone that is rich with other tones as well. It's easy to understand why crowds would gather and listen to him speak, because the sound of his voice is captivating. Aside from the first impression of being a baritone, I could distinctly hear different pitches within the same voice that harmonized with the louder baritone. It was amazing to hear, because it made his voice like a song. The different vibrations that I was able to pick up were not so distinctive that one would think it odd, only very beautiful. It is a strong voice, a persuasive voice, and the love and compassion he feels for all of us was also in the sound I heard. I will never forget it.

"There is nothing, absolutely nothing you could ever do that will stop me from loving you," he continued. "so remember that if you remember nothing else. Have you murdered? I still love you. Have you abused your child? I still love you. Do you think I can't love you because you're homosexual? Are you black, are you white, are you rich or poor? Again I say to you, I love you exactly the way you are. Now, loving you does not necessarily mean that I approve of all your actions. If your actions are causing harm or pain to others, then my wish for you would be that you stop those particular actions and begin to cultivate and express a more loving attitude. When you commit those acts that are harmful to others, you shut yourself off from me. My desire is that you come to know me and you cannot come to know me unless you have love in your heart."

"How do you go about cultivating love in your heart? The first thing to do, whether you actually feel it or not, is to act it out. Show an outward expression of love, even if you know you are not actually feeling it. The idea here is to begin to develop a loving heart, so the intention is most important. The intention should be a goal of being a loving person. Do those things that are kind and loving and the feelings will follow. Actions beget feelings; feelings beget actions. When you commit acts of harm, this results in feelings of anger and hate. Anger and hate result in actions of harm. Therefore, practice acts of love and kindness and you will cultivate your love for others and for me."

"There are one or two things that I would like to comment on regarding the religion that was set up after I left the physical existence. First of all, I had no intention of having a religion set up under my name. My reason for coming was to teach people about the Love of God and hope that they would open their hearts to Love. Then, as now, I desire only that you open your hearts to God and love one another as God loves you. It is very interesting to me that there are so many different religions in the world and even more amazing, is that there are so many different religions bearing my name! Religion is not going to bring you to God; only Love will. There should be only one Religion: LOVE."

"Now, you may ask yourself, what do I mean when I say LOVE? There are many kinds of love. There is the love a mother feels for her child; there is brotherly or sisterly love, and there is sexual love. But when I speak of the Love of God, I am referring to an omniscient love; a love that encompasses the full understanding of all things good or bad, including the knowledge of you prior to your life, during the life you lead now and including the greater reality beyond your life. The different loves I mentioned before, mother, brother, sister, sexual; these are all conditional type loves and though they might be construed as Love from God, they are insignificant compared to the unconditional love of Agape."

"Upon birth, all mankind has the ability to love unconditionally. Although you do not have that ability to the degree or extent that God does, you do still have the ability to love and be loved unconditionally."

"It is a sad fact of society that you are overly protective of your personality; of your ego. You have been taught not to talk to strangers; not to go up and hug a person until you know it is safe. I am not saying that you should tell a child to suddenly forget all those warnings and just start loving unconditionally, because it is too probable that he or she would then be preyed upon by somebody with ulterior motives or sinister plans. But do realize that in the name of protecting yourselves, you have inhibited your God-given ability to love unconditionally; so much so that it is almost impossible for many people to give or receive love. This is the result of societal teachings over thousands of years. To love is instinctive and God given, and since the average human baby has that capability at birth; this means that in the first few years of life he or she is taught not to love unconditionally."

"You CAN relearn to be more loving. On a global scale, there is no reason why everyone cannot culturally recondition themselves. Yes, it may require several generations to relearn to accept each other unconditionally, but it can be done if you make the effort. When enough of you open yourselves to Love, you will notice a decrease in rape, murder and other violence. Just as important; the negative impact of crime will be more tolerable. Even with the positive attitude of Love, will heinous crimes still occur? Yes, in all probability they will, but that does not mean that it is better to be inhibited, neurotic or fearful. It is better to have loved unconditionally than to have lived a long time in a safety net of inhibition and fear, even if it means sometimes being harmed! If you are hurt in someway, or if you have failed in your attempt to love, you are still better off for having tried."

"As easily as you were taught to live in fear and distrust, you can retrain yourself and others to love. Granted it may take a similar amount of time to recondition your culture and to retrain society into being more loving and more receiving, but it will never happen unless you take the first step!"

"The effects of loving can be seen clearly, quickly and easily and each of you can be more accepting of inappropriate behavior without responding in a negative way. Often there are many rewards to compensate for pain and suffering when one has an awareness of God. With all of my heart, I urge you to begin to express Love again."

"I have just one more comment to make. My blood is not going to save anybody; but my Love saves all. It is true that no one comes to the Father except by me. But you have misunderstood that statement. It does not mean that a person has to become a "Christian" in order to be saved. A person can be saved by Love without ever hearing my name uttered. Truly I say to you, if a person has Love in his or her heart, they know me well. A person may profess to follow me, but if he or she does not know Love, then they know me not at all. ALL will come before me when the physical body has finished its task on the Earth. There is not one of you who will not come before The Christ. Christians may experience me as Jesus, but someone who was a Buddhist, may experience my Light as Buddha. A Muslim might see me as Mohammed. I say to you that I Am that I AM, and all will know and acknowledge me when before me."

Jesus then stopped, unfolded his legs and stood up. He stretched fully, reaching up to the sky, then bent over and touched the palms of his hands to the rock underneath him. "Ahhhh," he sighed, "that feels good." He straightened back up, then sat down next to me, taking my hand in his once again. "And now, Susan, I am going to explain what I meant when I said 'I am you and you are me.' I will also explain that by understanding that statement, it is even more important that people learn to love one another. To do this, I need your assistance, because if you experience and understand what I am talking about, you will be able to relay that information better to others yourself. It's easy enough for me to say, 'what you do unto another you do to yourself or; what you do to another you have done to me.' Those two statements are very true, but what do they really mean? Put the physical body aside; also put aside the personality and ego. At the heart of you and everybody on this earth, you are spirit and in that unity of spirit there is only the one. Therefore, the I AM that is at the center of you is the SAME I AM that I AM. It is the same I AM that is at the center of each and every one of you. Therefore, how can you hate your fellow man? How can you do harm to another when the reality is, you are harming yourself?"

Jesus then clapped his hands together and rubbed them vigorously in anticipation. "Alright Susan, we are going to do a little exercise. I will assist you in going beyond the words I have spoken to the real understanding of what I mean. Are you ready?"

Now, I have to admit I wasn't really certain I was ready, but I looked him in the eyes and nodded my head affirmatively.

He smiled gently at me, "Have no fear, Susan, you a about to receive a great gift." He placed his right hand my back and I felt distinct warmth where his han touched the area around my heart. He kept his hand o my back as he began speaking again. "Susan, I just war you to relax and stare into space like you taught yourse how to do when you were a very young child. Sto thinking; move into that space you call your zone."

With his assistance, I easily moved into that space c being where I felt relaxed and at peace. He spoke agair "Susan, I am going to assist you in experiencing the Lov of God. Your experience will move you into the poir where you experience yourself as the Love of God, an when you experience that, you will understand 'I am yo and you are me.' Now, I am going to say some words an I want you to repeat the sentences after I say each on Do you understand?"

I nodded again and as he began to say these words, repeated:

"On this day, at this very moment, I give up th identity of Susan and become the Love of God. I AM Love, I AM Light. This is who I AM. Love is my name Light is my name. I love God; God loves me and I accep that Love as who I AM, so that I can be a vessel of tha Love to bring to all people so they too can know God God is Love and I AM Love. The Heart of who I AM i. Love. My mantra from this day forth is: I AM the Love of God."

There. Right there. It was only a nano second; a flash But again there was a stop in time and I could clearly see a...wall. I could see through it. I suppose it was ar energy barrier of some kind. I saw it. Looking at it, I discovered I could see through it, but not clearly. There was something beyond it, but I could not make out what that was. Then, as I watched, a ripple occurred and the wall dissolved in front of me. I felt myself moving into that place and that place was LOVE. I became that Love. The Love was GOD. I was Love and I was God and I couldn't tell where I ended and God began. We were one and the same. I wasn't so much in a place where I was thinking or even that aware of knowledge, but more just in a space of BEING LOVE; total, unconditional, non-judgmental, Love, Love, Love. I felt joy and peace and more. I had I AM realization. I didn't have to become the Love of God, because I realized that I already AM that! My realization was I already AM the Love of God! That IS who I AM! I have always been that. The gift was the realization; the recognition of that. In addition to that, I could see the duality of the "I" in third dimension. I now saw the understanding of how, even with a population of approximately six billion people on the earth, we are still ALL ONE through the identification of I AM. The I that is me and the I that is YOU is still the same "I". IT is GOD. I knew from this moment on, I would never be able to look at any person; whether it be friend or stranger and not see myself, I AM.

I felt his hand slide away from my back and I knew that this time we had spent together was over. We both stood and I tried to keep the tears from my eyes as I asked, "Will I ever see you again?"

He laughed softly and reached out, "Come here," he said, enfolding me in his arms for a warm hug. With my eyes closed, I gave heart-felt thanks for this moment. "I love you, Susan." He told me, "You know, I can hardly wait until we are both in heaven so I can show you just how much I *really* love you. Remember that I will always be with you, never separate from you. Keep your heart open and you will always be able to feel my Love."

I opened my eyes, and as I knew I would, found myself lying in the bed at the Valley View. The radio was still playing; no time had passed. I did not get up to write, or pace, or ponder. I simply lay there, as tears ran down my face, and I marveled at the Love I was feeling in my heart.

CHAPTER NINE

Some things don't change and my appetite is one of them. At 8 AM I was sitting in Ham's, eating a full breakfast. I did not expect to see Janet, nor did she show up. I did not bring my journal with me to write about my experience with Jesus. He had told me he would help me when the time came and I trusted that.

It's difficult to describe the mental and emotional state I was in. On one hand, I was supremely happy and content because of my newly acquired awareness of God and Love. On the other hand, I was also feeling rather dazed as I was still processing an extraordinary amount of information and today was also my last day to spend in the mountains, before I returned to my family and home. As much as I looked forward to seeing them, I was also a little worried about the reaction they might have when I shared my week with them. I was no longer the same person I was when I first started the week. What kind of impact was that going to have on my life?

I mulled through breakfast, then decided I would head up to Grand Father Mountain for my last day of hiking. When I arrived I walked out onto and across the swinging bridge to the ridge cliff on the other side. There, in the same spot where we had met the first day, was Janet.

"Solomon," I greeted her as I plopped down beside her.

"Grace," she answered, then we were both silent as we viewed the awesome vista before us. After a while, Janet spoke. "Going home today?" she asked.

"Yeah, later this afternoon."

"Are you going to tell your family what happened?"

"Well, yeah, I guess. I mean, even if I don't say anything right away, if I send this information to a publisher, I might not have any choice! I don't know if I'll tell them as soon as I walk in the door, or wait awhile. Either way, it won't make much difference. They're going to think I'm crazy when I do. I mean, I thought YOU were crazy when I first started talking to you! What in the world are they going to think when I tell them about all this?"

I felt a stinging slap on my thigh. "Grace! Have you learned anything at all from this week?!"

"Hey!" I laughed, even as I rubbed my thigh; "I'm still processing, okay?"

She turned and looked at me with a raised eyebrow. "I suggest you process a little faster, Suuussaaannn."

"Alright, alright," I acknowledged, "I know I'm not suppose to care what people think, but it's hard not to, when the events have already made a major impact on my life. I can't help wondering what's going to happen."

"I understand that," she responded, "but I can tell you that your life will be much easier if you'll remember that it's not important what other people think about this. You see you're looking at the situation all wrong. You've had some major experiences and right now you're thinking this is all about you. That, my friend, is where you are completely off base. This week has not been about you at all. This week has been about a message, and your only part in it, is that you have been asked to deliver it. You're a messenger, Susan, and that's all. Some people are going to love the message; some will hate it. Some people are going to admire you for what you've experienced and some will revile you. It makes no difference at all. People have free will to believe whatever they want to believe, or experience what they wish. It's all up to them and that's a beautiful thing regardless of which way they go."

I nodded my head, "Yeah, yeah, I'll try to remember that."

"I'll make sure you do," she answered, sticking out her hand. In it was a personal calling card with her address and phone number. "Put this in your wallet and don't lose it. Do you have email?" she asked and I nodded affirmatively. "Perfect. My email address is also on the card. Use it."

She watched as I put the card away. "Care to do some hiking?"

"Sounds like a great idea," I answered, as we rose to our feet and started out.

NAMASTE

Quick Order Form
Angel Crossing Publishing

Name:_____

Address:_____

City:_____ Zip:_____

Telephone: ( )_____

Please send me _____copy(ies) of Angel Crossing.

1-5 Books   @ $10.95 copy
6-75 Books   @ $ 8.76 copy
76 and above   @ $ 6.56 copy   **Book Total $_____**
                                  Sales Tax $_____
                                  (6% Sales Tax)

Send Check or Money Order to:
Susan Kaney
c/o Angel Crossing Publishing   **Shipping & Handling $_____**
14440 Southbridge Forest Dr.   **Total Amount Due $_____**
Charlotte, NC 28273

*Please allow 4-6 weeks for delivery.
Outside the U.S. 8-12 weeks.
Shipping and Handling: $1.00 for each book,
Maximum $10.00
Prices, Shipping and Handling Charges
may change without notice.